'I Know You Don't Love Lee.'

He spoke imperiously, fiercely. 'Promise me you won't marry him.'

Loretta shook her head. 'I can't, Paul—I just can't!'

'You can and you will!' Without giving her the chance to speak he reached out to grip her wrist and jerked her to his hard body. His mouth descended on hers, crushing it beneath his own.

'Promise!' he ordered, his lips caressing the delicate hollow of her throat. 'Obey me, Loretta . . . or else. . . .'

ANNE HAMPSON
currently makes her home in England, but this top romance author has travelled widely and lived all over the world. She has the same impetuous streak as her heroines, and it often lands her in the middle of a new adventure— and a new book.

Dear Reader:

I'd like to take this opportunity to thank you for all your support and encouragement of Silhouette Romances.

Many of you write in regularly, telling us what you like best about Silhouette, which authors are your favorites. This is a tremendous help to us as we strive to publish the best contemporary romances possible.

All the romances from Silhouette Books are for you, so enjoy this book and the many stories to come. I hope you'll continue to share your thoughts with us, and invite you to write to us at the address below:

Karen Solem
Editor-in-Chief
Silhouette Books
P.O. Box 769
New York, N.Y. 10019

ANNE HAMPSON
To Buy a Memory

Silhouette Romance

Published by Silhouette Books New York

America's Publisher of Contemporary Romance

SILHOUETTE BOOKS, a Simon & Schuster Division of
GULF & WESTERN CORPORATION
1230 Avenue of the Americas, New York, N.Y. 10020

ISBN: 0-671-57185-0

First Silhouette Books printing November, 1982

10 9 8 7 6 5 4 3 2 1

Map by Ray Lundgren

America's Publisher of Contemporary Romance

Printed in the U.S.A.

Chapter One

The green hills of Dorset swept gently down to the cliff which made a precipitous drop to the sea. Above, the sky was sapphire tinted with gold where the sun's rays caressed the filmy edges of lacy cirrus, floating cirrus, teased by the wind.

Loretta Sedgewick stood barefoot on the sand, nuzzling her toes into the warmth while her heart beat a throbbing tattoo as she saw at last the man she had come here to meet. Her face became animated, her deep blue eyes alive with eagerness and love. A soft smile parted her lips as the man drew nearer and she saw that he responded.

'He's far too old for you,' her mother had chided a few hours earlier, anxiety shading her eyes. 'Forty, and you a mere eighteen. Do you realise, child, that when he's fifty you'll only be twenty-eight, and the children's father will be old enough to be their grandfather?'

'I love him, Mother, and so what does age matter?' But a doubt had been born which refused to be crushed no matter how hard she tried. Nevertheless, there was nothing in her greeting to reveal her secret as she extended eager hands and said, 'You made it, Lee! I felt so happy when I saw you coming round the bluff!'

He took her gently in his arms and all her doubts fled. How long for? A shadow passed over her eyes.

'Dearest, what is it?' Lee kissed her before she could reply. 'You look troubled, sweet.' He held her from him, his brown eyes all-examining. She noticed the grey at his temples, the fine-drawn lines along the sides of his mouth; she glanced at his hands, where blue veins were showing. . . . It seemed that she was aware of these things for the first time, she mused as her eyes lifted from his hands, which were holding hers, to his face again. Now she realised that his skin was not nearly as clear as Philip Darlington's, the boy next door who several years ago had sworn he was going to marry her when they grew up. A sigh escaped her as doubts returned; she looked at the man she loved and spoke frankly to him, telling him what her mother had said when she knew her daughter was going out to meet the man whom Mrs. Sedgewick wished with all her heart had never come into Loretta's life.

'Mother's very upset about you and me,' she said finally, and to her surprise Lee was nodding his head and his eyes were slowly darkening. A frown came to his forehead and stayed there.

'Twenty-two years is an awful lot, darling,' he said at last, but drew her close all the same, as if he would not look upon her face and see the reaction to his words.

She pulled away, a tear bright on her lashes. 'We love each other,' she whispered huskily. 'I told Mother that age isn't important.'

He looked at her and she knew he was troubled and sad. Why, she thought rebelliously, had she been born so much later than he?

'Men don't live as long as women—'

'How do you know that? It's an old doctor's tale!'

Faintly he smiled. He thought: She is so very young, too young to face the realities of life. 'It's been proved, dear. And so, if we suppose—'

'I'm not supposing anything! Why, it is the most foolish and unprofitable thing to do!' Her tiny foot lifted from the sand and came down again heavily. 'You're young now so what does the future matter? We could both be killed together in a car or airplane crash.'

'Darling,' he said patiently, 'you've just said it's foolish and unprofitable to suppose anything, re-member?'

'I want to marry you,' she stated firmly. 'Let the future take care of itself!' And she lifted her face, offering him her lips, which he took, passionately . . . and yet she sensed a difference. . . .

'Let us walk along and sit down,' he suggested. And as they walked he asked if she had told her mother she wanted to marry him.

'Of course. I know you haven't asked me yet, but it's what we both want—and know we shall have,'

she added defiantly as an afterthought, but again
Lee was shaking his head. They sat down on a rock
ledge and his arms slid about her slender waist.
Again she lifted her face; he did not take the offering
of her sweet young mouth but stared at her instead,
taking in the firm yet feminine contours of her face,
the delicate blue veins beneath the fragile covering
at her temples, the curving brows above eyes so
expressive they told you everything. He touched her
golden hair, tenderly, lovingly, and then he closed
his eyes and his lips moved convulsively.

'I'm too old for you, dearest.' The words seemed
to stick in his throat, so hoarsely were they spoken.
'Far too old, Loretta. You see, dear, although it is all
right now, and would be five years hence, afterwards, when I am fifty—'

'I shall be only twenty-eight. Yes, Mother told
me—just in case I was so dumb I couldn't count!'

'No need for that,' he admonished in that stern
voice which had thrilled her from the very beginning. 'Your mother does happen to be right. She's a
mature woman with a great deal of good common-
sense, whereas you are a mere child who wants
something so badly that she is too stubborn either to
be advised or to look for herself and see what is
likely to happen—what *must* happen, for we can't
stop the clock, you know.'

She wanted to retort that she did not care but the
doubt was strong now, built up by Lee's assertions,
which were merely a supplement to her mother's.
Was she a mere child? Wanting her own way so
badly that she refused to listen to those with more
sense than she? Yet why should she listen! She had a

mind of her own; she had made her choice and that was that!

'I want to marry you,' she said and added that she wanted the wedding to be soon.

'There's nothing to wait for,' she added. 'I can be ready in a couple of weeks.'

Lee had to laugh. 'My child, it is usual for the lady to wait to be asked.'

'We're living in modern times.'

'Pity, for if we hadn't been then you'd have had to wait until you were twenty-one for your mother's permission to marry.' He paused but she made no comment and he went on, taking her hand and absently passing a thumb over the back of it. 'I think, my love, that we ought to wait a while—No, please let me finish. I have a suggestion and it is this: I've been offered a job as estate manager on a large citrus farm in South Africa. I feel I should take it and go there on my own. After six months I shall write to you—'

'Six months! Six whole months!'

'—to say if I still want to marry you,' he continued, ignoring the interruption. 'If I do not write, it will mean that I have had second thoughts—that I feel the age gap is far too great.' He had turned away so she saw only his profile. But she realised just how difficult it had been for him to voice those words and she knew he was deliberately hiding his expression from her. She swallowed, trying to relieve the dryness in her throat, for she knew that Lee would not budge from the decision he had just made.

'You're cruel!' she cried. 'Have I no say in this matter?'

He looked at her. 'You know you haven't,' was all he said for the moment. But when she remained silent he added gently, 'If I do write, dear, and you still want to marry me, then you will come out to me in Africa. However, during the six months you yourself might have second thoughts and decide to call the whole thing off—'

'I never shall! And I shall die in six months!' she told him tragically.

'If you have changed your mind,' he went on with only a slight smile to denote his hearing of her complaint, 'then you will ignore my letter.' Again he looked at her, holding her chin firmly in his hand. 'Is that all very clear to you, Loretta?'

Her mouth twisted convulsively. 'You're cruel,' she repeated. 'How can you bear to leave me for six months when you love me—? Perhaps,' she said accusingly, 'you don't love me at all but have only been playing around. And taking this job in Africa is the way you have chosen to get away from me now—now th-that you're—t-tired of—of m-me!'

He took her in his arms and kissed her tenderly. She felt him quiver against her and said contritely, 'I'm sorry, darling. I know you mean it for the best—well, what in your opinion is the best for me—' She shook her fair head vigorously. 'But it isn't the best, Lee! Oh, please, don't do this to me! It isn't for the best, I tell you!' she added as his face hardened.

'It is what I believe is for the best,' was his quiet assertion after a pause. 'It's the honourable way and one which I mean to follow.'

'But the choice is all yours and that's not fair!'

'Initially the choice is mine, yes. Afterwards, should I write to you, then the choice will be with you.'

That was all. Argue she might, but without success. Loretta tried for days but finally she found herself seated opposite to Lee in a restaurant, eating a farewell dinner which she felt was choking her.

She looked down at the cake her friend had made for her, then, stooping, she blew out the candles.

'I feel quite old,' she said, but laughed as she sat down opposite to Maura who, since the death of her mother when she was twenty, had had a small flat on the outskirts of Dorchester, the city in which both she and Loretta worked. Loretta now shared the flat, for her own mother had died eighteen months ago leaving her alone in the world, except for an aged aunt whom Loretta saw only about twice a year. 'Twenty-five and on the shelf!'

'Only because of your own choosing.' Maura passed her the knife and Loretta cut the cake. 'I sometimes wonder if you had a disappointment in love when you were young.'

'Funny you should say that,' reflectively as Loretta passed a wedge of cake over to her friend.

'You mean—you did have a disappointment?' Maura looked curiously at her across the candle-lit table which she had set with such care a couple of hours earlier, while Loretta was out—sent out deliberately to do some shopping for the week-end.

'I was eighteen. . . .' The story was unfolded in a matter of sixty seconds and there was very little expression in Loretta's voice as she uttered the final words, 'He didn't write, so he mustn't have wanted me after all.'

Maura was frowning heavily. 'He was far too old for you and he obviously knew it.'

'Oh, he knew it all right and so did everyone else—except me.'

'You must have known he was too old, must sometimes have seen yourself a widow, your kids fatherless when only comparatively young.' She shook her head, her brow still creased in a frown. 'He was a gentleman, honourable, and I hope he is happy even though I do not know him and never shall.'

'He liked the country and so I feel he will be happy on the land.'

Maura bit into her cake. 'You know nothing of what happened to him, nothing at all?'

Loretta shook her head. 'No, how could I? He didn't even leave me his address—said it was for the best in case he decided he wouldn't write.' She gave a wry grimace. 'I expect he knew I'd worry him with letters, so he guarded against it.'

'You don't seem upset about it all.'

'After seven years? I don't feel anything. I can't now even bring his face into focus.'

'He'll be forty-seven.'

'I know,' she mused, wondering how she would feel were she to come face to face with him at this moment. 'It's a funny thing, Maura, but I was so sure he would write, so confident that he'd not be strong enough to resist marrying me.'

'Well, he obviously was strong enough.'

Loretta merely nodded her head and changed the

subject, saying she must pay a visit to the village where she had lived with her mother until eighteen months ago. 'I've a few friends and acquaintances whom I correspond with as you know,' she went on, 'and they're always asking when I'm going back to have a day seeing them all.'

'Want me to come with you? I'm free on Saturdays now that we have extra staff.'

'Will you? I'd like the company. We could go in my car.'

'It's settled, then.' Maura took another bite of the cake. 'Next Saturday?'

'That'll suit me fine.' Loretta was looking forward to the visit, but little did she know what an upheaval it was to bring about in her life.

She drove first to the old school which had been converted into a delightful house some years ago after the school closed, its pupils having been gradually reduced until there were only a dozen or so left. Mrs. Drinkwater lived there with her middle-aged daughter, a spinster so attractive that it was a puzzle to everyone that she had never married. The two greeted the girls cordially and offered them tea and cakes. The next stop was at a small cottage on a hill occupied by an ancient widower who always used to be telling Loretta that he would like to become her stepfather. Mr. Wilkins also offered them tea, but apologised for not having any dainties to give them.

'Times have become hard for us pensioners,' he said with a deep sigh, 'and so cakes and biscuits and the like have to be given the go by when you've to budget the way I have.'

'Don't worry, Mr. Wilkins.' Loretta smiled. 'We've just had more than we wanted at Mrs. Drinkwater's.'

'She's a fine cook. Makes some tasty cakes, and now and then brings me a couple. Much appreciated —kindly of her, yes. kindly.'

The last call was at the post office where Miss Pilgrim had been the postmistress when Loretta was there. Miss Pilgrim was an eccentric and no mistake, and so absent-minded that if you left her a parcel it was hit or miss whether it caught the next post or one a week later. She had left a fortnight ago, Loretta was told by the new people, a Mr. and Mrs. Greason who had already been doing the place up.

'But you must come in,' said Mrs. Greason when Loretta would have turned away. 'Come and see what we are doing to the place.'

The two girls entered, unable to say no to the smiling invitation. Mr. Greason was plastering the living-room wall and his young son was cleaning up the mess he was making.

'It's a good thing we have our Saturday afternoons off,' he was saying a short while later when again the girls were drinking tea at the kitchen table. 'It gives us a day and a half every week. What a mess the place is in, though! Miss Pilgrim wasn't all that old that she couldn't do something towards keeping the property in good order.'

'You should have seen the rubbish and old letters and the like we've found behind the shelves—You'll remember the shelves, Miss Sedgewick?'

'Yes, she kept so much on them that we always

wondered how she'd go on if ever she decided to move.'

'There was a sort of cavity behind them and it's our opinion that when she became inundated with clutter she swept the lot into a heap and tossed it into that cavity.'

'Let the young ladies take a peep at what we removed,' suggested her husband. 'Or have we burnt that lot along with what we took from the utility room? Gee, that was cluttered, I can tell you,' he added turning to the girls. 'We had to shovel it out into the yard and there we set fire to the lot.'

'We haven't yet burnt the rubbish we found behind the shelves.'

'Then take them and show them.'

The girls exchanged glances which plainly said they weren't in the least interested in Miss Pilgrim's accumulated rubbish, but at the same time there were gestures of resignation for they had no intention of snubbing these charming people. And so they left their tea to go into a shed in the yard and there they just stood and gasped.

'Letters!' exclaimed Maura. 'Letters which, presumably, had not been delivered to their owners.'

'Letters and other papers—forms gone brown with age, and even money. We found two ten-pound notes and one fiver.'

'And stamps,' put in her husband who had come behind them.

'But it's the letters,' persisted Maura bending down to pick one up in spite of the dust and grime. 'Some people—expecting letters. Why, it's criminal!'

'She was very absent-minded,' inserted Loretta, herself stooping to pick up an undelivered letter which was yellow with age. 'Mrs. Gregory. I knew her. She died when I was about sixteen.'

'Mr. Wentworth,' murmured Maura, now fascinated. 'Who is he, I wonder, and did he suffer disappointment when this never arrived—' She stopped abruptly as Loretta, her face drained of colour, stood staring down at an envelope she was holding in a hand that trembled. 'What's the matter?'

Loretta swallowed hard. She held forth the envelope, pointing to the stamp. It was at the name which Maura was looking and her lips parted slowly. But no words came. Instead, it was Loretta who said, 'My letter . . . from Lee. Look at the date. . . .' Tears gathered in her eyes even though there was no pain in her heart. It had all been so long ago . . . seven years . . . 'He wrote . . . but had no reply. He thought I had changed my mind, believed I'd let myself be persuaded not to marry him.'

'Miss Sedgewick, what is all this about?'

The voice of Mr. Greason came to her from a long way off, but she looked up and said in a voice scarcely audible, 'This–this was from a man I l—A man I once knew.' She had almost said a man she had loved, then realised that gossip would be flying round the village and she had no wish for that. 'You can see it was for me—' Again she held it out, this time in front of Mr. Greason, though his wife's head came forward too. 'I'll take it, if I may?'

'Certainly you can take it. But look at the date! Was it something important . . . ?'

'What a question!' Maura was exclaiming ten minutes later as she sat beside Loretta in the car. ' "Was it something important?" '

'Fate,' murmured Loretta, putting a hand to the pocket of her dress and hearing the paper rattle. 'It wasn't to be that Lee and I should marry.'

'I reckon fate was doing you a good turn,' was her friend's quiet rejoinder. 'By now, love, you'd be regretting the impulsiveness of youth.'

'Perhaps.'

'No perhaps in it. He's forty-seven now. We were saying so the other day—on your birthday. Three years off fifty.'

Loretta gave a sigh but said nothing. She was anxious to read what had come for her so long ago. Poor Lee, waiting for a reply and as the weeks and months slowly passed he would have had to accept that he had lost her, lost her because of his own act in going away. Yes, poor Lee. Loretta's soft compassionate heart ached for him and she wished she could go to him now, but that was impossible simply because she had not the money for the air fare to South Africa. She had helped Maura with decorating the flat; and, like Maura, she had treated herself to new curtains and covers for the bed and settee which she had in her room. There was the repair to the car, not paid for yet, and she needed some new clothes and shoes. Hard it was to make ends meet, what with the rise in rent for the flat, the big electric and telephone bills. . . . You tried to reduce them, but even if you did the rates would go up so you were back to the beginning again. No, she could not possibly go out to South Africa to see Lee.

The contents of the letter were brief to the point of austerity.

Just to let you know, dear, that you were right when you wanted to marry me. I miss you so now it is with you.

Love,
Lee

Loretta showed it to her friend later, once they had arrived back at their flat.

'I want to cry,' quivered Maura as she handed it back. 'Even though I know in my heart it was for the best.'

Loretta looked at her as she folded the paper and put it back in the envelope. 'You seem so sure.'

'I'd not like to think my husband was forty-seven and me only twenty-five.'

'But I shall now die an old maid.'

'Rubbish!'

'I never seem to take to the ones who take to me.'

'You've a crush on Derek Spencer, that's why.'

'A married man with a wife he adores and two of the cutest kids alive.'

'He's something, though.'

'And more!'

'Well, he's not for you, so you might as well start looking elsewhere.'

'I don't think I want to bother. I'm very happy here with you.' She was looking at Maura as she spoke and now she found herself frowning and asking if anything were the matter.

'What could be?' Too careless the tone and the

manner of Maura as she glanced away towards the window which overlooked the antiquities—the Roman remains of a house and wall—which were beautifully displayed with surroundings of well-cut grass and some shrubs and trees.

'You seem strange—somehow.'

'I don't quite get you.'

'Come off it!' Loretta knew for sure there was something the matter. 'Is it a secret?'

'Is what a secret?' procrastinated Maura, but she was soon being persuaded to 'spill the beans' as Loretta had put it. 'I've met someone nice—it was love at first sight as you might say. I didn't tell you because he went away only a week after we'd met, but he writes and I know he'll propose when he comes back in a couple of months' time.'

Naturally Loretta was taken aback, but her response was swift and sincere. 'I'm so happy for you, Maura. Will you be married right away—what I mean is, soon after he returns?'

'I feel he'll not want to wait very long,' answered Maura frankly and with a blush which spoke volumes.

'So you'll want the flat?'

'To tell the truth I haven't even thought about it. Ron and I haven't reached that point yet and he might have plans for buying a house. After all, this flat isn't very big.'

'But plenty big enough for two,' Loretta was quick to point out.

'I suppose it is.'

'Do you want me to begin looking round?'

'Not yet.' Maura frowned. 'Oh, let me think more

about it first! I too have loved having you round, sharing the flat with me, and the expenses. I was grateful when you came as I'd been having nightmares about what a flatmate would be like—and how I'd get rid of her if we weren't compatible.'

'Let me know as soon as you can, Maura, as it's not easy to find a comfortable place to live at the price I can afford.'

'I'll give you plenty of warning,' promised Maura, who was still frowning, a sign of unhappiness, and her friend was swift to assure her that, were the positions reversed, she would be just as eager to get married.

'After all, it's one of those things we each knew could happen,' she went on with a smile. 'It could have been I who had found someone.' Her thoughts flew quite naturally to Lee . . . and she was wishing she had the money for the visit to South Africa.

Fate . . . She was thinking again of fate when, only ten days later, she had been summoned to the offices of a Dorchester solicitor and told of her aunt's death and the will she had left. She was handed a letter and she sat there, reading it and feeling glad she had always made the effort to go and see Aunt Alice because, living in an Old Folks' Home, she had little pleasure in her life—at least from the outside world. Loretta's mother had made her promise always to make the effort, and now Loretta had nothing to reproach herself for because it was less than three months since she had made the long train journey up into the Lake District to see the old lady and spend a few hours with her before returning to Dorset the same night.

'My dear Loretta,' she read, 'you must do as you like with this little legacy, but I would be happy to think you would spend it on a holiday—a cruise or something equally romantic. I want you, dear, to buy a memory with it if possible but, as I have said, it is yours to spend as you please and you might just consider a holiday to be an extravagance.' It was signed and there were two crosses after her aunt's name.

To buy a memory . . .

'Have you any idea what you will do with this money?' inquired the solicitor merely for conversation and to break the silence which followed Loretta's reading of the letter, for she seemed to be sunk in thought.

She glanced up. 'Yes, I do have an idea,' she replied with a smile. 'I'm going to have a holiday in South Africa.'

'I know I should do something more sensible with it,' Loretta was saying ruefully a few hours later when she and Maura were having their evening meal. 'But it was Auntie's wish that I go for a holiday, and so that is what I intend to do.'

'You can take a holiday elsewhere.' Maura was concerned, fully aware that, because she was feeling unsettled now at the flat, Loretta was going to Africa solely to find Lee and see if he still wanted to marry her.

'Of course I can, but I want to see Lee. I have his address now, so unless he has moved I can find him easily. If he *has* moved, surely there'll be someone who can tell me where he is.'

'You're crazy!'

'I haven't said I intend to marry him, Maura,' laughed her friend, but Maura was not amused.

'If he asks you, then you're lost!'

'He's nice, Maura,' responded Loretta nostalgically. 'We had such happy times together.'

'He wasn't so old then.'

'He could be very young for his age.'

'And it could be the opposite! He could be crippled with—with gout or something of the kind!'

'Gout?' Again Loretta laughed. 'He was as fit as an athlete.'

'I don't suppose he's as fit as an athlete now.'

'What of your Ron? Do you expect him to be senile by the time he's forty-seven?'

At that Maura had to see the amusing side and she joined her friend in laughter. 'It's just that I'd like to think of you marrying someone just a little older than yourself—five years older would be just about right.'

'Thirty. Well, who knows what is in store for one?'

'You might meet someone there if only you'd not jump into anything with Lee.'

'I'm seven years older now, remember. I was impulsive at eighteen, but I've sobered up a bit since then.' She looked affectionately at her friend. 'Take that troubled frown off your face, love. I shall promise you I'll not do anything silly, or make a decision I am likely to regret.'

Chapter Two

The fiery sun was sinking rapidly, shedding burnished golden rays over the silent bushveld, causing it to smoulder beneath a mist of orange smoke. Loretta stood on the *stoep* and cast an appreciative eye over the whole impressive scene. She sighed, though, and wondered if she had done the right thing in coming out here, to this part of Africa where she had hoped to find Lee, and perhaps happiness and contentment. But Lee was away for two weeks, taking a holiday in Durban. His home was all closed up and so his employer had suggested she stay in his house until Lee arrived back home.

Paul Tremayne . . . Tall and handsome and confident. An Englishman who had lived on the citrus estate all his life, his father having inherited it from a distant cousin who was an Afrikaner. His home, a rambling colonial style mansion—or that was Loretta's description of it, since it seemed to have the proportions of a mansion—stood in extensive grounds filled with exotic trees and flowers, with sweeping lawns and fountains, a swimming pool and tennis court and many shady paths and arbors.

Paul Tremayne . . . Arrogant and critical in his initial examination of her . . . and there was something very strange about him whenever she mentioned Lee. Paul was hiding something and she felt she must in the end ask him what it was.

She had managed all right to arrive here, having been able to hire a car and driver at the airport. She had previously written to Lee, telling him she was coming but he had already left and as a result was not at the airport to meet her. When she arrived it was to find the house closed up and in a sort of panic she had gone up to the front door of Rikuyu Lodge and a few moments later she was inside the house waiting for the owner to come to her. The black servant had obviously been told, on carrying her message to his employer, that she was to be shown into the sitting-room and this was where she met Paul Tremayne. . . .

From the first moment something had stirred within her; she had felt the fine golden hairs rise on her forearms, had experienced feathers along her spine, had wondered why her pulses had quickened; and the answer to all this was that she was in a panic, for she had nowhere to lay her head that night—unless of course there was a town nearby and an hotel. In a panic. . . . Why, then, did she find her eyes glued to that handsome face? That had nothing to do with fear. She was examining every detail from the dark brown hair to the wide forehead, the straight dark brows above piercing eyes that were tawny brown, and then she was looking at his other features, the high cheek bones, the lean, aquiline quality of his face in general, the mouth which though thin was somehow sensuous . . . and she found herself thinking of what it would be like to feel those lips on hers.

Staggered by such thoughts, she lowered her head, but not before the keen eyes of Paul Tremayne had caught sight of her risen colour. She heard his dry tone inquiring what was the matter and knew that he was mocking her, fully aware that he was having some profound effect on her. Temper was difficult to control as she felt it rise within her like something physical. He had obviously become used to women being affected by his magnetism, his dynamic personality—to say nothing of his superlative good looks. Around thirty, she decided, but with all the confidence of a mature forty or more. She wondered if he were married and had since learned that he was not. But he was probably contemplating marriage, she thought, and felt an inexplicable tinge of dejection and—was it anxiety?

Why she should care whom he married not only puzzled but irritated her. Olga Davenport might not be what appealed to women but there was no denying she possessed all that any man could desire —beauty, figure, and wealth thrown in as a bonus to the man who chose her for his wife.

'Enjoying the sunset?' The voice was dry and satirical; she turned to look up into his face, a bronzed face with tiny lines fanning out from the corners of the eyes, lines created by his narrowing his eyes against the fierce African sun.

'Yes—it is beautiful.' She paused, feeling extremely awkward, and said in a hurry, 'It's so lovely and cool now, after the awful heat of this afternoon.'

'January is one of our hottest months.' He moved, his steps long and smooth, and stood by the wooden railing against which Loretta was leaning, but a few yards away. She cast him a sidelong glance and he turned before she could examine his profile. 'We're south of the Equator and so the seasons are a reversal from what you have in England.'

She nodded automatically, still feeling awkward in his almost godlike presence. He seemed so magnificent that he not only overawed her but made her decidedly uncomfortable.

And yet she found herself hoping he would not leave her yet awhile. . . .

'I believe you have frost in July? That seems strange. . . .' Her voice trailed away to a self-conscious silence. She was talking for the sake of it and realised by the sound of her own voice that she was hoping to gain confidence.

'Winter is June through August.' Dry the tone and edged with amusement. 'How long are you expecting to be here?'

'I haven't given it a thought.' Three days had passed since her first encounter with the wealthy owner of Rikuyu Lodge and the vast estate which went with it. 'I wish I'd been able to see Lee before he left.'

'As I explained, you only just missed him by one

day. You've to wait another ten days before he arrives back.'

'He always goes away for his annual break?' Paul had told her that Lee was the manager of the estate, but Loretta rather thought that 'under-manager' would be more appropriate, as she could not imagine Paul Tremayne handing over the reins completely to anyone else. He would be in on everything himself, she decided, and woe betide those who might be foolish enough to shirk their duty.

'Not always, but this year was a little different.'

She looked swiftly at him. Again she had detected that strangeness in his manner and the added unfathomable inflection in his voice. She hesitated, then asked him outright if there was anything she should know about Lee.

'I've told you why I am here,' she added. 'The letter which was never delivered—' She spread her hands. 'I haven't kept anything back.'

The keen tawny eyes rested on her for one silent moment before he spoke. 'You are thinking that I'm keeping something back?' His jaw had hardened and his mouth seemed just a little thinner than before.

'Yes, I feel sure you are keeping something important from me.' She did not know what to expect, but certainly she did not suppose that Lee was married, otherwise she would have been informed of it right away.

She was, therefore, staggered when after another pause she was hearing her companion say, 'Lee is married, Miss Sedgewick—has been for the last three and a half years.' He had turned, so that he could be sure of noticing her reaction.

'Married?' She had given a start, but now all he saw was a sudden pallor spreading over her cheeks. 'Then why didn't you say so immediately? I'd not be staying here if I'd known he was married.'

A strange, unfathomable silence followed her words, and as she stared inquiringly into the bronzed countenance she had the most odd impression that he had kept the truth from her in order to keep her here! But that was absurd! Why on earth should a man like Paul Tremayne wish to keep her here?

'Perhaps it was because, although he is married, Lee is separated from his wife—'

'Separated!' she cried, a deep sadness darkening her eyes. 'You mean, he isn't happy?'

The fine mouth curled in what could only be described as a sneer.

'How can any separated couple be happy? They live with the knowledge that they've made a mistake —one of the most serious mistakes one can make in one's life.'

'I'm sorry to hear that he's separated. Where is he now, then?'

'As a matter of fact, he's gone to Durban because his wife is there. I guess he hopes for a reconciliation, but perhaps Flora is not cut out for this kind of life. At all events, she has gone back to her parents.'

Loretta said, avoiding his eyes, 'How old is she?'

'Much older than you,' was his immediate reply. 'I believe she's in her mid-thirties.'

'I see. . . .'

'How old are you?'

'Twenty-five.'

'Lee is almost fifty—'

'Forty-seven,' she inserted quickly and saw his mouth lift at the corners in that sardonic way which was beginning to rile her.

'Forty-seven's not far from fifty. He's old enough to be your father.'

She frowned. This man was suddenly becoming far too familiar. At first he had been remote, unapproachable . . . but now. . . . She tried to move but failed as he took a step which brought him closer to her.

'We were in love,' she said and Paul threw back his head and laughed.

'You told me your mother died eighteen months ago. When did your father die?'

'When I was seven.' Her eyes had moved; she was fascinated by the long lean fingers resting on the rail, brown fingers, flexible, with a hidden strength beneath that sun-scorched skin.

'Then it is plain that you regarded Lee as a father—'

'No such thing!' she denied hotly. 'He was not in the least fatherly in his attitude towards me.'

At that she found her body subjected to a long-lasting appraisal while he allowed his eyes to rove from her face to her throat and to the delicate slope of her shoulders. She felt the colour rise in her cheeks as he rested his gaze on the firm contours of her breasts and wished absurdly that she had put on a loose-fitting shirt instead of this dress, which fitted snugly both to her breasts and waist before flowing out in a circular skirt which, though hiding her lower curves from his interested eyes, yet at the same time was probably tantalisingly intriguing to a man as plainly observant as the one who was causing her to blush and to fidget and wish she were somewhere else.

As if he understood her feelings and enjoyed his ability to affect her in this way his expression changed to one of sardonic amusement and his voice fully reflected this as he said, 'No, I don't suppose he was. It would be difficult for a man to treat a woman like you in a fatherly way.' His eyes lit with humour as her colour deepened. 'Nevertheless, on your part, it was a father and daughter relationship, even though you might not have been aware of it.'

'You obviously consider yourself to be something of a psychologist,' she flashed, eyes sparkling in a way that seemed both to attract his interest and his admiration. She felt that although he would be undisputed master in his own house he nevertheless would not want his wife to be totally without spirit.

'One has no need to be particularly clever to draw those conclusions.' Suddenly he seemed remote, indifferent, and she wanted to hold his interest, to keep him with her. All most illogical since she disliked the man exceedingly, considering him to be far too sure of himself, too arrogant, and too condescending towards herself. She thought of his girlfriend, who had come to dinner the night before last, and she wondered if Paul ever treated her in this high-handed way. Loretta rather thought that Olga would be able to give almost as much as she received, for she too had been arrogant, condescending towards Loretta and obviously not pleased to find her there, staying in Paul's home. Her voice had been curt, her questions impertinent, of the kind which almost made Loretta forget she was a guest in the house of the girl's man friend. Nothing would have afforded Loretta more satisfaction than to retaliate but instead she had managed to remain calm and even friendly in her conversation with the girl.

'I suppose,' said Loretta at last, 'that as long as Lee is married I ought to be thinking of leaving, since there is no longer any point in my staying.'

To her surprise he frowned almost darkly at her and she again had that inexplicable impression that he wanted her to stay. His next words served to strengthen the idea as he said quietly, his eyes fixed on her face, a strange expression in their depths, 'As long as you've spent your legacy on this trip you might as well make the most of it. It would be foolish to leave now, after only a few days.'

'But—' She stared at him bewilderedly. 'Is there any point, Mr. Tremayne?'

'I did mention that he is separated.'

'But hoping for a reconciliation.'

'That was merely a conclusion I had come to and it could be a wrong one.'

'If he should come back with his wife—'

'Then you could begin to think of leaving,' he broke in curtly. 'Meanwhile, be my guest and enjoy your stay.'

Her eyes widened. 'Be your guest?' she echoed. 'How long for?' Why was her heart beginning to race, her pulses becoming erratic?

'For as long as you like.'

'You mean—even after Lee returns?'

'I feel you'd be better here, where there are

servants living in, than staying alone with Lee—that is, presupposing he returns without his wife. Lee has no servants living in, just a houseboy who goes in daily and returns to his family in the *kraal* at night. Should Lee have his wife with him then you'd have no alternative than to stay here, in my house.'

So cool, this shaping of arrangements for her! Who did he think he was, telling her what she must do? Had he made a courteous invitation she could have accepted, but as it was she asked curtly if there was an hotel in the town of Falburg which was no more than five miles away.

'I'll stay there until I can arrange a flight back home,' she ended with a tart inflection which brought his straight dark brows together in a frown which made her feel like a child about to be reprimanded.

'Firstly, it would not be proper for you to stay there alone, and secondly, it is not a comfortable hotel. You'll be wiser to accept my invitation and stay here.' Firm the tone and implacable the light in those tawny eyes.

Much to her chagrin Loretta found herself saying, almost meekly, 'If the hotel really is uncomfortable then—then I accept your invitation.'

'Well, as long as that's settled I shall leave you. I have work to do in my office.'

She watched him go, conscious of new emotions as her eyes followed the lithe swinging gait then moved to the broad shoulders, proudly squared below that arrogant head. What was the matter with her? Never before had she felt like this about a man. No, not even Lee at their most intimate. Could Paul Tremayne be right when he declared the relationship on her side was that of father and daughter? She frowned and pushed such thoughts from her mind for she felt they were almost unhealthy.

She stood a long while, with darkness spreading gently over the orchards and the silent bushveld beyond. The moon rose from behind a long line of *kopjes*, resplendently argent in a sky of lilac which was rapidly changing to deep purple as the transient twilight faded altogether and the hush of night was broken only by the distant throb, throb of a drum-beat. This was Africa, primitive and beautiful, and she felt she had left the civilised world behind forever. Peace enfolded her as she stood there and it was of Paul Tremayne she was thinking when it should have been Lee . . . Lee who was married. . . . He had probably waited a long while, just to see if she would write to him, promising to come out here and marry him. So lonely and sad he must have been, and disillusioned, taking it for granted that her love had not proved strong after all.

These thoughts had already occupied her mind earlier in the day but now, in this primordial atmosphere of darkness and peace, it was Paul who occupied her whole mind and she was powerless to dismiss his face from her mental vision. There was something so vital about him, so magnetic and irresistible. . . .

That was a strange word to use, she thought with a sudden frown. What was there to resist, anyway? He was a near stranger, an African citrus grower who had offered her hospitality, and that was all.

She turned at last, yet paused to take a final look

at the scene which was now more plainly visible in the light of a full moon, an enormous moon, it seemed to Loretta, and she supposed it took on these proportions owing to the crystal clarity of the air. The *kopjes* seemed eerie, the veld unending, the line of trees along the dry riverbed like sentinels standing in sinuous formation. Yes, all was primitive, and a little frightening. For the whole aspect spelled loneliness, isolation from all that was civilised and tangible. She moved towards the lighted window through which was the sitting-room, moved slowly and reluctantly, for it was pleasant in the solitude even though it was awe-inspiring as well.

Dinner was served at eight o'clock and she wondered if Olga would be here but to her relief she was not. Still, she did feel she would have been more comfortable if someone else had been coming. All so illogical because, on the other hand, she knew a thrill of expectation at the idea of dining alone with the man whose personality had made so deep an impression on her senses.

He was immaculate in a suit of white linen and a frilled evening shirt of pale lilac. His hair shone with cleanness and from his body came the heady smell of after-shave mingling with that of newly-laundered linen. Loretta was in a long dress of apricot cotton trimmed at neck and hem with lace in a deeper shade. Her waist was adorned with a belt studded with sequins, a contrasting belt of soft black velvet. Her hair had been brushed till it shone; her eyes were bright and smiling, her lips softly parted to show even white teeth. She knew she was looking good but she seemed to be waiting breathlessly for

Paul to tell her so—and the next moment she was angrily telling herself that she did not give a damn whether he admired the picture she made or not.

'You look charming,' was his comment at length and her soft blush brought a swift smile to his lips. Pompous creature! Aware of what he was doing to her like this! Why couldn't she be cool and off-hand, poised as Olga had been, keeping all emotion imprisoned beneath the veneer of cold indifference?

'Thank you,' she returned demurely.

'Shall we have a drink first?' With the flick of a hand he indicated a chair and she sat down in it while he walked silently to the drinks table and picked up a bottle. 'Same as last night?' he said and she nodded at once.

'A dry martini, please.'

He brought it to her, standing for a space staring down into her lovely face. The moment was fraught with tension as if an electric current was shooting back and forth across the room. Her hand trembled as she took the glass from him and she saw that firm mouth lift at one corner in that particular way he had, which to Loretta denoted sardonic amusement, and she almost asked him what it was all about. But of course she refrained, remembering she was his guest and, therefore, it was incumbent on her to remain polite no matter how much his varying moods and mannerisms aroused her anger.

'What goes on in that beautiful head of yours?' he asked after sitting down opposite to her and relaxing his long body against the cushions. 'Some women are transparent while others remain mysterious to the end.'

'You've had a lot of experience with women—?' She stopped, appalled at the question she had never meant to utter. 'I'm sorry,' she began, when he interrupted her with a swift and imperious flick of the hand.

'No need to apologise; it was an obvious question to follow what I had said.'

'Nevertheless, I ought not to have asked it.' Loretta picked up her glass from the small antique table at her elbow and took it to her lips. She was embarrassed and knew he was enjoying her embarrassment.

'Yes,' he admitted, 'I've had my share of experience.'

She managed to lift her eyes and meet his half-amused gaze. 'And now? Are you thinking of settling down?'

A very strange pause followed before he said, 'I guess it's time I found myself a wife. A man reaches the stage where he would like to see his children around him.' He was watching her intently, his tawny eyes still flecked with humour.

'Is that the only reason—what I mean is, surely the wife is more important than the children?' What kind of a conversation was this? Loretta asked herself. It was becoming more intimate with every moment that passed.

'Depends on whether or not one marries for love,' was Paul's unexpected answer.

'You'd not marry without love, would you?'

'I might have done—' He stopped with an abruptness that made her start, and she saw that all humour had left his face.

38

'What do you mean?' The question was automatic —a follow on to what he had said, as it had been before.

'I've been thinking for some time that I would like to become a father.' Quiet the tone and Loretta felt sure he was in reality talking to himself and not to her. 'An estate like this ought to have an heir.'

'We were talking about love—' Again she pulled herself up, and this time he did not smile at her embarrassment.

'Ah, yes, love.' A cynical note had now entered his voice. 'Have you ever been in love, Loretta?'

Loretta. . . . So naturally it had come out, and she liked the way he said it, in that finely-modulated tone of his.

'You know I have been in love.'

'With Lee?' He shook his head. 'That was not real love, as I've already implied. Surely there have been others since then?'

She shook her head, saw the sceptical light in his eyes and her own eyes sparkled militantly. 'Although you might not believe me—there haven't been others since then!'

'Not the flimsiest of affairs?'

'If by that you mean a light flirtation—well, I am not interested in that kind of an affair.'

To her vexation she had provided him again with something to laugh at and this time his humour was audible as he threw back his head and laughter escaped him.

'What rot! Everyone these days is interested in light flirtations.'

'Everyone?' with a lift of her brows which might

have been a reflection of his own haughty gesture at times.

'Well, anyone with your kind of attraction.'

'You deliberately try to embarrass me,' she complained and took up her glass again.

'Are you trying to convince me that flattery embarrasses you?' he inquired sceptically.

'I see no reason why I should try to convince you of anything,' she retorted, almost incensed now by his attitude. 'After all, we're strangers, aren't we?'

To this he shook his head and reminded her that they'd known one another for three whole days. She had to laugh and saw his eyes widen and take on an inscrutable expression.

'Three days is nothing.' She spoke for the sake of it, in order to break the silence which followed her laughter.

'A great deal can happen in three days,' he murmured almost to himself, the inscrutability of his expression reflected in his voice.

She felt tense all at once, as if she were on the verge of a profoundly important discovery. She was vitally conscious of a physical awareness of him, of a draw which was almost indomitable; she seemed to be fighting against something which she knew would overwhelm her in the end. She heard herself saying briefly, 'Such as?' and wondered if she were deliberately tempting him.

'There is such a thing as love at first sight.'

She stared, not having expected anything like that. What did he mean? 'I had the impression that you were cynical about love.'

He made no comment on this and in fact deliberately changed the subject, asking if she had any plans for her holiday here.

She shook her head. 'There isn't much to do, is there?'

'You want activity?' he asked with a curious inflection and again she shook her head.

'I shall be quite happy taking walks and relaxing in the garden.'

'Both of which can cause you fatigue at this time of the year, especially when you're not used to the heat.'

'I shall be very careful.'

'You'll need to be.' He glanced at his watch and frowned. 'What's the matter with Ngugi? He's late with the dinner.' But the houseboy appeared at that very moment, a big, brawny man with a perfect physique and the kind of face one would like to paint if only one had the ability.

He smiled, then said with a hint of apology, 'Some small thing go wrong, Mr. Paul, but dinner is ready to be served now.' He withdrew without having to explain what it was that had delayed the meal.

Paul rose after draining his glass and Loretta followed suit. He stood close—far too close, she thought, unnecessarily close, and looked down into her face for a long moment in silence. Embarrassed, she averted her head; it was brought up again with a firm hand beneath her chin and instead of resenting the action, which was imperious to say the least, she merely stared up into those tawny eyes and wondered what strange thoughts caused them to glitter like this. Passion. . . . She thrust away the idea but it persisted. She was alone in this house with Paul, but for the servants he had earlier mentioned and which, he had intimated, would give her protection. She continued to stare . . . and knew he intended to kiss her. With a swift movement she was free but only for a short moment. He took her by the wrist and brought her to him; she tried to struggle and then gave up, imprisoned as she was in what seemed like hawsers of steel. His body, too, was hard against her own soft and slender frame. She quivered but could not move as he ran his hand smoothly down her spine.

'I'm going to kiss you,' he began and before she could utter the indignant 'No!' which came instantly to her lips her mouth was claimed and crushed in a masterful and possessive way that left her panting for breath. She tried to speak, to voice a protest, but she had first to gulp in air and when she paused he took her lips again, took them in a sensuous kiss that seemed to last for an eternity and to which she was in the end compelled to respond. He had made her, forced her to his will . . . and she had enjoyed every moment of it!

A sort of horror followed seconds of self-recrimination as she again tried to pull away from those imprisoning arms. To have responded! To have parted her lips and allowed his probing tongue to enter. . . . His mouth was now finding other delightful places as, with the expertise of the lover to whom nothing is new, he caressed with his lips the hollow in her throat where the pulse beat wildly and visibly, out of control, as was the throbbing beat of her heart. His hands were not idle; they slid down her spine but at her renewed struggles and little cry of protest they stopped and instead of roving as she knew was his intention, she felt them pressed to her waist, almost encircling it. The sensation was glorious . . . a mingling of helplessness and excitement, for he had her totally in his power. She had never known that to be totally in a man's power could be so exhilarating, so hedonistic, stirring emotions that could only be described as sensual—primitively sensual for she wanted more . . . much more.

He held her from him at last, his eyes filled with mocking amusement. 'So this is the girl who has just said she isn't interested in flirtations.'

Shocked into reality by his words, she backed away, shame colouring her cheeks. Tremblingly she brushed a hand through her hair and to her dismay she felt the sting of tears in her eyes. 'You were a cad to do that!' she flared, taking refuge in anger. 'It was no way to treat a guest in your house!'

Laughter lit the tawny eyes and curved the fine lines of his mouth. 'Calm yourself, little one,' he advised. 'We're about to go in to dinner and servants have a way of interpreting the kind of look you have on your face at present.'

'Stop laughing at me!' Loretta actually stamped her foot. 'It isn't in the least funny!'

He came to her, because she was crying, and because she looked so distraught—afflicted, almost. Gently he took hold of her hand and drew her close. His lips took hers, gently this time, their touch a mere caress designed to soothe.

Bewilderedly she stared up at him through eyes misted by tears, and she shook her head from side to side as she said, in a choked little voice, 'I don't understand you, Mr. . . .' It sounded ridiculous to call him Mr. Tremayne after what had happened.

He thought so too because he said, his cool moist lips against her cheek, 'Paul. It's a short name so it shouldn't be difficult.'

'Paul. . . .' She spoke the name as if compelled to do so by the expression in his eyes. 'I don't understand you,' she quavered, feeling exceedingly foolish as the repetition left her lips.

'Perhaps, my child, I do not understand myself,' was his cryptic rejoinder as, bringing out a handkerchief, he gently dabbed the tears from her eyes.

Chapter Three

Two days later Loretta said she would like to go into town. 'I need to buy a few items,' she added, but then asked how she would get there. 'I know you don't have buses—'

'Buses?' That plainly amused him. 'Who is there to use buses?'

'The locals for one, and people like me.'

'There aren't many people like you. This is no holiday resort, as you will already have gathered. As for the locals—well, they rarely go into town and when they do they walk. Five miles is nothing to them.'

'You mean—I must walk?'

'No, I'll run you in. Shall you need to be there long?'

'About an hour,' she estimated.

'Then that's all right. I have a few things I want myself.'

'I'd like to get my hair done one day,' she began. 'It's not the same when I wash it myself.'

He looked at it and there was admiration in his glance. 'It looks more than all right to me.'

She shrugged, determined not to blush at his flattery. 'I'd rather have it done at the hairdresser's if that is possible?'

'Can you drive?'

'Of course.'

'Then you can use the runabout whenever it is free. Lee uses it mainly, so while he's away it is yours if you want it.'

'Thank you very much.' The mention of Lee set her thoughts flying to the day when he would be home. He had no idea she was here and she was now concerned in case he should resent her coming, since all that had been between them was long past. He was now a married man—and somehow that hurt only in that his marriage was not happy. She felt no pangs either of regret or jealousy and had already owned that time had more than healed any hurt she had suffered at his leaving her to take up this post so very far away. 'Shall I use it today?'

'No, I'll take you in and show you around—not that there's much to see,' he added wryly. 'A few shops, a bank and a few administrative offices and that's about it, except for the Club and the small hotel I mentioned.'

'Club? Is there a social club?'

He nodded his head. 'The Acacia Club, where we dine and dance and indulge in gossip.'

'I can't imagine you indulging in gossip,' she said and he nodded in agreement.

'You play polo?' She had heard that most of the farmers played polo and imagined Paul would be a member of a team.

'I do, yes, when I have the time.' They were in the garden, where Paul had come upon her cutting flowers for the house. And now he was looking down at her, regarding her with a keen scrutiny . . . wanting her to colour up, she thought and deliberately turned her head away. The sun above was fierce and she had put on a wide-brimmed sun hat, but now they were under shady trees and she had taken it off and it was lying on the ground beside the basket in which were roses and lilies which she had cut a few minutes before Paul joined her. 'You're already getting a most attractive tan,' he commented after a while. 'It suits you.'

She said nothing, but bent to cut another rose and drop it into the basket.

'What time do you want to go into town?' he asked and she said she would suit her time to his. 'Most obliging,' he returned with a hint of mockery in his voice.

'I'm your guest,' she reminded him, 'and the first prerequisite of a guest is to consider her host.'

'Very proper,' he applauded and the mockery was still there. 'If we go now we can have lunch at the Club. They don't do anything exciting at lunch time but it will be a change for you and I can introduce you to anyone who happens to be there.'

'Thank you.' She put on her hat and then picked up the basket. 'I'll get ready at once.'

* * *

The road was dusty and dry, and ochre-coloured in the sun. Some smart bungalows nestled in the low hills at either side, their gardens bright with flowering trees and shrubs.

'We're lucky around this particular region,' Paul told her. 'The Zilam River, tributary of the Limpopo, rarely dries up, so we are fortunate in rarely being short of water. So you will find flowers growing profusely and lawns looking green for most of the year.' He went on to tell her that there was no real summer and winter as such, but only a wet and dry season. She listened with keen interest but suddenly her attention was diverted by a dainty little fawn crossing the road a long way in front of them.

'Oh, look! Isn't it lovely!'

Paul cast her a sidelong glance. 'Have you not seen any of them on the estate?'

'No—do they come so close to the house?'

'Often they do. But mainly you'll see them further afield than the actual gardens. Deer are usually shy, timid creatures.' It had disappeared as swiftly as it had come into view, hiding itself in the low bushes at the side of the road.

The town was just one main street with shops on one side and the library and public buildings on the other. Paul stopped at the filling station and introduced Loretta to the proprietor, Stan Golding, who looked at her both with admiration and curiosity.

'On holiday?' he asked, plainly hoping for some information he could pass on to the next customer.

'Sort of,' answered Paul for her. 'Miss Sedgewick's a friend of Lee but by some mischance she arrived the day after he'd left for Durban.'

'So she's staying with you?' He transferred his gaze to Loretta again. 'Enjoying it?'

'Very much.'

'You chose the hottest time of the year.'

'Yes, I believe so.'

He filled the tank and took the money. 'How long are you staying?'

'I'm not sure,' she said evasively and glanced at Paul, hoping he would put a halt to the man's questions, which he did by starting the car, and driving away after saying goodbye to the man, who was still curious.

'We'll be filling the mouths of all the gossips.' Paul's tone was indifferent. 'You'll not have to mind. There is little to entertain the people and a bit of gossip helps to pass the time.'

She laughed. 'I won't mind. After all, I came of my own accord and if I didn't think too much about people's reactions then it's entirely my own fault. As a matter of fact,' she went on reflectively, 'I didn't think it would be quite like this—not so remote and away from everything.'

'Didn't you look on the map?'

'The map wouldn't have been much good. One has to have a starting place before a map becomes useful. All I had was the address, which seemed very vague, but I was assured by the travel agent that I'd not have too much difficulty in getting here.'

'And you didn't, although it's a long way from the airport.'

She remembered the drive through miles and miles of thorny acacias interspersed with grassy plains. And then she had come to the valley with the mountains as a backcloth. The low, rambling colonial homestead had stood out against the green of exotic trees and bushes, and the sky had been clear above, azure blue tinted with gold.

She had been excited, thinking of Lee and expecting a warm welcome. . . . Well, she had no regrets about coming, for even though not one week had yet passed she was happy and contented and very much at home in Paul's house. He still overawed her at times, and his mocking satire riled her, but for the most part she and he got along in a friendly, companionable way that was entirely new to her, even excelling the rather special relationship she had enjoyed with Maura.

'We'll park here, in the square, and have lunch when we have finished our shopping.' He drove on to a bare patch of ground, his tires sending up a cloud of ochre dust as the vehicle crunched to a halt. 'Shall we meet back here in about an hour?'

'Yes, that'll suit me fine.' She was all awkwardness again and angry with herself because of it. She told herself there was no need for this uncomfortable feeling which at times assailed her.

'Shall you have much to carry?'

'Not anything large or heavy.'

'In that case I'll not give you the key. The library's over there, if you want to join.'

'I might, if I have time.'

They separated then, each going off in a different direction, but met later in the chemist's where, entering after him, Loretta heard him ask for a well-known brand of talc and after-shave. She was surprised that the shop would have these in stock, and even more surprised when another assistant supplied a customer with one of the most expensive perfumes on the market.

On being served Paul turned, smiled at her and went out without speaking. Loretta managed to get all she wanted and then went to find the stationer's, where she bought notepaper and envelopes and was also able to buy stamps at the same shop. Glancing at her watch as she came out she realised she had about twenty minutes to spare so she made her way to the library, a squat, red-brick building with a corrugated tin roof. A few straggly hibiscus bushes strove for survival in well dried out soil on each side of the door, above which was the word 'Library' in faded gilt letters. It was with a feeling of uncertainty that Loretta decided to go in, for she did wonder what sort of books she would find. The fact that Paul had suggested she join was, however, the deciding factor and much to her surprise she found herself confronted with well-filled shelves of excellent books, many of which were the latest best-sellers.

She looked at her card and saw she was allowed to take out three books, one of which had to be non-fiction, so she chose an old edition of *Impressions of South Africa* by James Bryce and decided with a wry grimace that Paul would instantly tell her it was well out of date. But never mind; she was not interested in politics, and the land did not change. It was the geography she was interested in, and such things as climate and flora. It was not very intelligent, in her opinion, to live in a foreign land and not learn as much about it as one could.

She arrived back at the car on time and Paul was just coming towards it, his tall lithe figure holding her gaze for she was, as always, fascinated by the air of distinction which set him high above any other man she had ever met.

'Did you manage to get all you wanted?' Paul unlocked the door and held out his hand for her parcels. These he put on the back seat along with his own. 'I see you went to the library.' He accepted the three books, glanced at the titles, and held up the one on Africa.

But before he had time to speak she said, with a hint of mischief in her glance, 'It's well out of date, isn't it?'

He looked at her darkly but there was humour in his eyes as well. 'So you guessed what I'd say?'

'Of course,' casually and with the merest hint of defiance in her voice. 'I want to learn about the land, mainly, and the flowers and animals. Those don't change, so any book will do, and I happen to know this is an especially informative one.'

'You are quite right; it is.'

He got in beside her and started the car. They took about a minute and a half to reach the Club, which was situated in rather impressive grounds where flowers grew in beds on the lawns. Trees provided plenty of shade and there were hedges of crimson hibiscus and pink and white oleanders. The building was low and white, L-shaped, and she soon discovered that the shorter piece was the restaurant, while the other was the ballroom.

However, there were tables and chairs at the back, in a shady garden bounded on one side by a most colourful rockery and on another by a grenedilla hedge at the back of which stood a row of jacaranda trees.

'Would you prefer to sit outside?' he asked, then warned her that she might be attacked by mosquitoes.

'I've sprayed,' she told him. 'I always do because they'd have me if I didn't.'

They sat down and a waiter in white coat and trousers brought them the menu.

Loretta chose melon for a starter then settled for a salad and cold chicken. Paul had the same.

'I did warn you there wouldn't be much choice,' he said on taking the menu from her and passing them both to the waiter.

'I very much enjoy salad,' she said, then stopped to stare at the girl who had just entered the restaurant through a side door which was just visible from where she sat. Paul did not see her and after a mere second's thought Loretta decided not to tell him that Olga was here. Paul was glancing around and after spotting a couple just sitting down he beckoned to them and stood up.

'Can I introduce you to Miss Sedgewick, a guest of mine?' He smiled at the girl, a pretty little thing with dark brown hair and merry brown eyes. 'Loretta, meet Mr. and Mrs. Byers—Susie and Charles.'

'How do you do?'

'Happy to meet you.' The handshakes over, the couple stood for a few moments, chatting and showing polite interest in Loretta without asking too many questions. She liked them on sight and readily accepted when they invited her over to their farm for afternoon tea the following Saturday.

'They have a small general farm—part dairying and part for growing produce such as maize.' He told her where the farm was and how she would get there.

'They're young to have their own farm,' commented Loretta, her eyes following them as they went back to the table they had chosen. 'Susie doesn't look any more than twenty.'

'She's a little older than that. About twenty-two, I guess.'

'It's still young.'

'The farm was left to them, or, rather, given to them by Charles's uncle, who'd had enough of Africa. He couldn't make the place pay, and no wonder, he was always at the bottle.'

'Charles is making it pay now, though?'

'Just about. Real prosperity in their line of business takes time.'

'You obviously prefer citrus fruit.'

'My place was always a citrus growing estate. We grow, in addition to the oranges and lemons, clementines and also a smaller variety of tangerine.'

'It's all very interesting to me.' She smiled at him across the table, her eyes wide and limpid, her lips quivering slightly for no reason at all.

He said after a prolonged and unfathomable pause, 'Could you settle here, do you think?'

She wrinkled her nose, a little gesture she had when trying to make a decision.

'Yes, I believe I could. The heat would take a bit

of getting used to, but I'd do it eventually.' She glanced inquiringly at him. 'Are you thinking that perhaps Lee and I will get together after all—that he and his wife will decide to have a divorce?'

Paul's face hardened unaccountably. 'You believe in divorce?'

'I'm practical. If two people can't get along then why should they live in misery together when they can be happy with someone else?'

The tawny eyes were narrowed almost to slits and the jaw was taut. 'You'd not mind having a divorce, then?'

He was angry and she would have liked to know the reason. However, she had no intention of asking him and so she answered his question instead. 'Like all women, I would hope my marriage would last forever.' She smiled again but her eyes were vacant, faraway, as if she were picturing something in the future, something pleasant, and extremely precious. His full attention caught, Paul sat and stared at her, watching every small change of expression, and so intent was his gaze that she could actually feel the probing examination, as if he were endeavouring to read her very mind. Her attention was brought away from thoughts of bliss and rapture with the husband she would one day have, brought with suddenness to the man opposite to her and she felt a tinge of colour rise to brighten her cheeks. Silence stretched and so did her nerves. This was another tense interlude, similar to one that had gone before and she had the same strong feeling of electric currents in the air around them.

'So you're an idealist?' The silence was broken at

last but before she had time to reply the waiter was at the table, bringing their meal. When he had gone Paul repeated the question.

'I suppose I am,' she admitted. 'But there's nothing wrong in it,' she added almost defensively.

'Nothing at all. In fact, everything is right about it.'

She said, eyeing him curiously, 'Are you an idealist, Paul?'

'Not that I knew of.'

'Knew?' she repeated, and he gave a small start as if it had taken the word to remind him that he had spoken in the past tense.

'I suppose I should have said—not that I *know* of.'

'So you're not an idealist, then?' She had no idea that her voice was edged with disappointment, and even if she had she would have been unable to find a reason for it.

'I'm a realist.'

'Then in that case you should believe in divorce.'

'Not necessarily. But what makes you suppose I do not believe in divorce?'

'Your manner. I can tell you don't.' She paused to let him comment, but he remained thoughtfully silent and she added presently, 'Divorce is so sad, isn't it? A couple meet and fall madly in love and they want each other so much that often they can't wait—I mean,' she amended hastily as she saw the sudden curve of his lips, 'they find the waiting unbearable—'

'You were right the first time, my dear,' he interrupted dryly. 'They can't wait. They don't need to these days with modern science being what it is.'

The subtle inference made her blush and she was glad to see the waiter appearing with a tray.

'Do carry on with what you were saying,' he urged. 'It promised to become interesting.'

She shook her head. 'I had finished,' she said.

'No, you hadn't. You were about to open your heart to me—'

'No such thing!' she denied hotly. And then, inconsistently, 'I was only about to tell you what I think of love and marriage—but it doesn't matter now.'

'You were about to say that although a couple may begin by being madly in love they often end up by hating each other. It's true, and you are quite right when you say that divorce is sad. I hope it never happens either to you or me,' he added finally and she cast him a swift and puzzled glance. For there had certainly been something strange in his tone, some undercurrent in his words, and something unfathomable in his eyes.

However, she decided to change the subject and for some reason talked about Lee, telling Paul a little more about her mother's objection to the friendship.

'She was so glad when he went away,' reflected Loretta. 'But I was heartbroken.'

'Had you managed to get over it by the time the six months had passed?'

She shook her head, not answering straight away as her attention was caught by a pretty little lizard sunning itself on the rockery. So still it was! How could any creature with heart and lungs and nerves remain as motionless as that? It was one of the wonders of nature, she thought, and sadly felt that man himself had travelled far, far away from what was natural.

A small cough reminded her that Paul was awaiting a reply and she told him that she had by no means managed to get over her love for Lee—in fact, it had been stronger than before.

'I was so convinced he'd write, you see,' she admitted. 'I felt sure he loved me too much to let me go.'

'And now?' Something profoundly intense about him now, with those tawny eyes boring into her as if he would read her mind without waiting to see what she would say.

'Strangely, I feel nothing.' Sadness edged her voice because she felt she had lost something very precious. 'Even the knowledge that he's married does not affect me.' She glanced at him, recalling her puzzlement that he had kept the knowledge from her at first, then, when she had asked for an explanation he had merely said that it was because he and his wife had parted. Loretta had then gained the impression that there was an altogether different reason . . . that Paul did not want her to leave.

And now he was looking at her with this strange, unreadable expression, and, without being able to explain it, she again had the idea that he did not want her to leave.

'Nothing,' he mused, lost for a space in thought, while he was absently buttering a crusty roll. 'You do realise that neither your love nor his was as strong as you supposed?'

'I can't agree, but neither can I disagree. A long absence is bound to bring changes in people. I had become resigned long ago to the fact that Lee did not want me after all.'

'It transpired, though, that he did want you?'

Loretta tilted her head in a little gesture of perplexity. 'Paul, why are you talking like this? I mean, you appear to have taken some personal interest in my affair with Lee.'

'I suppose such a situation intrigues me,' he returned with mild mockery. 'I am interested to see what will be the outcome of this visit of yours.'

'You consider me foolish to have come at all?'

He made no immediate response; it was as if he were torn between two different answers and when at last he did speak she felt sure it was not the truthful answer he was giving her. In fact, it was not really an answer at all, but just an evasion.

'Had it been I who received that letter after seven years I'd have thrown it away. The past is past and there is no profit in trying to recall it.'

'I didn't come here with the intention of recalling it.'

'Why, then, did you come?'

She considered a while before saying, in what she knew was a rather lame little tone, 'I guess I was curious. Fate seemed to be playing a hand, too, in the form of Auntie's legacy.' She paused a moment. 'I just had to come—but I don't expect you to understand exactly how I felt.'

What he would have said to this Loretta would never know, since at that moment Olga appeared, obviously having finished her lunch.

'Oh!' She stopped by the table and her narrowed eyes moved from Paul to Loretta and back again. 'I'd no idea you were here, Paul.' He had risen and was ready to give her his chair but she told him she had had her lunch.

'You can sit down all the same,' he invited and after a small pause she accepted his chair. Paul beckoned to a passing waiter who brought another chair at once.

'I was intending to take a stroll in the gardens.' Her eyes swept to Loretta, startling her by the sheer venom she saw within their depths. Surely the girl was not jealous of her! The idea left Loretta with nerves tingling. She looked at Paul and again knew those unfamiliar stirrings which affected both heart and mind. He was so attractive. . . . She caught her breath. No, she must not fall in love with him! It would be sheer folly—

'Then we might all three take a stroll when Loretta and I have finished.' Paul's polite voice broke her thoughts and she returned her attention to the contents of her plate.

'The Dobsons are giving a party on Wednesday and they want us to go.' Olga leant back in her chair and opened her handbag to take out a slim cigarette case which Loretta suspected was gold.

'You know I don't care for the Dobsons.' Paul's voice was almost cold.

'I accepted, nevertheless.'

'Without consulting me?' His brows had lifted and in his eyes Loretta noticed a sternness she had never encountered before.

'You can't refuse, darling.' Her voice was now a purr of persuasion. 'They're my good friends and it would be impossible for me to have refused the invitation. What excuse could I have given them?'

'You can go, of course.' Paul lifted a hand to hide a yawn, an action which brought a glint of anger to his girl-friend's eyes. But she was clever, decided Loretta, for when Paul looked at her he saw only a look of entreaty.

'Please come with me,' she begged. 'It would seem most strange if you weren't with me.'

As Loretta glanced from one to the other a most odd sensation swept over her. It was as if she were hearing Paul's saying that Olga and the Dobsons could go to the devil!

But what she did hear was, 'Very well, Olga. I'll come with you.'

Chapter Four

Loretta sat in the pleasant little parlour of Lee's house, listening to the clatter of crockery and cutlery coming from the kitchen. He had told her to sit down while he made the meal and she had obeyed. She felt very young . . . and obedient. Not a pleasant feeling but yet not unpleasant either.

She stared through the mosquito netting to the garden and the view beyond where the solitude of the veld seemed intense, the vast silence breathless, as if this were that one moment in time when the world was created. A distant drumbeat drifted through this silence, breaking it and yet adding to the impression of primordial isolation and solitude. She could see the mountains, hazed to a bluish-grey outline against the brittle azure of the African sky. There was the familiar mystery in the grotesque shapes of the *kopjes* which at this time of day were always in the shade; the trees too, baobabs and dome palms . . . they seemed all to be part of some fantasy of the mind and could not be real. Loretta felt she was a million light years away from towns like Dorchester and London, from villages like the one in which she had been born and raised. This was so vast, so frightening and yet so peaceful, a landscape still basking in the mists of time.

'It's ready.' Lee, so much older and yet still young in his manner, smiled at her and beckoned. She rose and came beside him, felt his arm about her waist and did not attempt to analyse her feelings at the contact. She did not resent it—no, on the contrary. Yet she could not thrill to it as she had in those days which now, more than ever, seemed so far away.

'What a lovely feast!' she exclaimed on entering the little dining-room and seeing the table set daintily with silver and glass and embroidered mats with matching napkins. 'You've become quite domesticated, Lee!'

'I've had to—' He pulled out the chair and she sank into it. She felt his cool lips touch her hair. 'Yes, my dear, I had to. Oh, I have the houseboy to come in and clean the place, and at first he did the cooking, but I'm afraid his ideas and mine clashed and so I decided to learn a little about how to prepare my own food.'

'And it was a big success.' She glanced at the salad in the big glass bowl, at the tray of various meats, at the crusty bread and, lastly, at the delicious-looking apple pie which Lee had put on a small side table within his reach.

He sat down opposite to her and said in the quiet,

cultured voice she remembered so well, 'Help your-self, Loretta, dear. I would have cooked but you did insist it wasn't necessary.'

'This kind of a meal suits me fine, especially in this sort of weather.'

'It's not getting you down, then?' His swift ap-praisal took in the honey tones of her skin on face and throat and arms. 'It suits you, dear.'

She smiled winningly at him. 'Yes, that's what Paul said.'

'Paul. . . . You've met Olga, I suppose?'

'Of course, several times.' She had been here for two and a half weeks, she thought, and it had passed so very swiftly.

'There's a rumour that they are about to become engaged.'

Loretta helped herself to a couple of slices of meat. 'You believe they are in love?' Her head was bent; she had no wish for Lee to see her expression.

'Love?' He paused and she could imagine him lifting his brows. 'I don't believe either is capable of love.' So firm the assertion, in a voice faintly edged with contempt. 'Paul Tremayne's a hard, unfeeling man and Olga seems to me to have no heart at all.'

Hard and unfeeling. . . . Loretta had not found him so, but that did not mean that she was convinced he couldn't be hard. She felt sure he could, if the occasion demanded it. She thought of the occasion when he had kissed her and she had responded. He had not referred to it since, and naturally she had not expected him to do so. What she *had* expected was that there would have been a repetition . . . and deep within her she had hoped for it. No use denying that Paul affected her so deeply that she could easily have fallen in love with him, and in fact she was not sure that she wasn't more than half way there already, even with the lack of encouragement. And now she had Lee, Lee who had been so thrilled to see her, after the first shock of surprise. Lee, who loved her and was willing to divorce his wife and marry her—more than willing, eager, and impatient.

'We could live together, darling, until the divorce comes through. No one takes any notice these days.'

She had not answered for it seemed that all her girlhood dreams were shattered by his suggestion—gone were the flowing white dress, the veil and the orange blossoms. Well, she'd not be the first to forego those things, those unessentials. Times had changed anyway, and the white dress was no longer traditional. No use living in the past; it was unprofitable, Paul had asserted, and he was right. The time was now, and she was here with Lee, the first man she had loved . . . the only man she had loved. A frown touched her brow and Lee asked her what was wrong. She had been seeing Paul's tall figure above her, had been thrilling to his kisses and his roving hands. She looked at Lee and said with a smile, 'It was nothing—just a thought. This meal is super! If you ever find yourself out of work you could buy yourself a restaurant.'

He laughed and she looked intently at him, aware of searching for what had thrilled her so much when he laughed in the old days. A sigh escaped her when she recognised nothing . . . changes again. . . . She felt sad because of the lines on his face, the added grey in his hair—in fact, it was mostly grey now, iron grey, though, so by no means unattractive. His eyes seemed not quite so alert, and he had put on rather more weight than he should have done.

It was the climate, he said by way of an excuse when she had commented on it.

He said, taking her empty plate and putting a smaller one in front of her, 'Have you thought about my suggestion, Loretta?'

She shook her head. 'It's a big step, Lee—and we have to get to know one another all over again in any case.'

'The tragedy of that letter!' Bitterness, deep and strong, caused his voice to become so harsh it grated on her ears. 'That stupid old woman! The damage she has done—and probably to others as well.'

'It was fate,' supplied Loretta quietly.

'I was so devastated when I had no reply.' He was walking away and the words came over his shoulder. 'I was so sure you loved me but the absence of a reply to my letter was proof that you had changed your mind.'

'And so you married someone else.' She hadn't meant to remind him of that but it had come out before she could stop it.

'After several years, yes—and it was the biggest mistake of my life,' he added bitterly.

'Is there no hope of a reconciliation?' She had asked the question before, having told him that Paul had believed he'd gone to Durban for the specific purpose of trying to persuade his wife to come back.

'None at all.' Brief the reply and curt. Lee went into the kitchen with the plates and returned with a jug of creamy custard.

'What is she like?' inquired Loretta curiously.

'Very pretty.'

'How old?'

'Over thirty,' was all he answered to that.

'It was perhaps a pity you didn't have a child.'

He was cutting her a wedge of pie but he stopped, the knife idle in his hand. 'You sound as if you wished for a reconciliation?'

'I feel that divorce is sad, Lee, and I also feel that, in your place, I'd have another try.'

He frowned as if in pain. 'So you're not in love with me?'

She bit her lip. 'Dear Lee, we've talked about this before. We're almost strangers again and I must sort myself out.'

'You came here for one obvious reason: to marry me—'

'No, I came because I was curious. What the outcome would eventually be I could not guess. Auntie's legacy provided the means for the trip; I decided to come but, as I've said, the outcome was vague. I do now feel that I'd half expected to return alone.'

'Even if I hadn't been married?' Lee placed the pie on her plate and poured custard over it.

'I can't say, Lee,' she answered, distressed. 'The fact is that you *are* married—'

'But ready for a divorce. Why can't you consider my proposal, darling, for I'm sure you must still love me, otherwise you'd have been married before now.'

She looked up into his face, wondering if he realised the import of what he had just said. For he himself had married.

'Can we just be friends?' she begged. 'Let us go about together for a little while until I know just what it is I want.'

'Of course.' He bent to kiss her brow before sitting down opposite to her. 'I'm a selfish brute to try and force you to a decision at this early stage. Forgive me, my love?'

She nodded dumbly. Words would not come from a throat that was suddenly dry and blocked. She was glad when it was time for her to leave. Paul was having a few friends to dinner and he had invited Loretta to be there.

'You seem to be very friendly with him.' There was jealousy in the tone which Loretta could understand.

'I find him charming,' was her frank response. 'We get along fine—which is as well, of course, since I am a guest in his house.'

'I wish you weren't.' They were at the door and as it was Saturday he was not working. He seemed so forlorn and lonely that Loretta almost wished she had not accepted Paul's invitation. 'If I'd been at home when you arrived you'd have stayed here.'

'No, I wouldn't. You don't have any servant living in. People would talk.'

'And would you care?'

'Yes, Lee, I would.' Her thoughts had flown to Paul, who, like everyone else, would have put the worst construction on the fact of her living alone in a house with the man she had once wanted to marry.

'But what if you decide to come and live with me, until the divorce, after which we could then get married?'

'If I decide to come and live with you then it would be different. We'd let people know that we intended to marry.' She was pale, for this conversation troubled her greatly. She was so sorry for Lee that she just couldn't say outright that the idea of living with him before marriage had no appeal for her whatsoever. She did not know herself whether it had appeal or not because her mind was so confused. Looking at Lee now she was struck by the fact that he was so much older than she, yet he was no older than he would have been had she married him seven years ago. He was the same man, kind and considerate, a thorough gentleman with high ideals and a high sense of honour. Yes, he was the same man . . . yet the changes seemed to make him different in a way she could not possibly have explained.

'I must go,' she said at length. 'I have to wash my hair and dry it, and that takes some time.' She glanced at her watch. 'Yes, I must go.'

'Enjoy your evening,' he said and there was no expression in his voice.

'Goodbye, Lee.' She lifted her face; he took it in his hands, gently, almost reverently, and kissed her quivering lips.

'Fate!' His voice shocked her with his harshness. The change in his manner was dramatic. His second kiss was almost brutal and she drew away, colour leaping to her face.

'Lee—that wasn't nice!'

'Forgive me—oh, Loretta,' he said in a strangled tone, 'why did it have to happen to us? Why did I leave you in the first place? You begged me not to but I stupidly felt I must do the honourable thing, because of this difference in our ages. And in being honourable I made a hash of your life and mine.'

'No, dearest Lee, don't say so.' Her eyes were stinging with unshed tears. She drew closer again and spread her arms about him, protectively. He shuddered against her, a man filled with regret, a man hungry for love. 'We'll manage to sort ourselves out, but for the present, darling, please be patient with me for I honestly don't know my own mind.' There, it was out, but she suspected he had known all along just how undecided she was.

'I'll be patient, love. Forgive me for kissing you like that.'

She lifted her face again and took a gentler kiss, and then, impelled by she knew not what, she flung her arms about his neck and snuggled her head against his breast. When she came away her vision was blurred by tears. She ran from him, down the narrow path, and only then did she realise that Paul was there, in the near distance, and he must have witnessed that last poignant little scene when, in an impulse to comfort, she had flung her arms about Lee's neck.

To her dismay Paul slowed his steps so that she was bound to come abreast of him as she reached the point where Lee's narrow path joined the much wider one leading to the extensive area of outbuildings which were hidden from Paul's house by a thick belt of trees.

'Enjoy your visit?' There was icy politeness in his voice which stunned her.

'Y-yes, thank you.'

'A grand reunion after all?'

'Not exactly.' She had told Paul only a few hours after meeting Lee that she did not think she and he had any future together and Paul had seemed satisfied out of all proportion.

'The little scene I witnessed just now must have meant something.'

'Lee was upset,' she returned briefly.

'And so were you by the look of things.'

She frowned. Drained as she was and on the verge of tears, the last thing she wanted was to enter into an argument with Paul. 'It isn't any of your business,' she began, then stopped, aghast at her rudeness to the man in whose house she was living. 'I'm sorry,' she added in a muffled tone. 'I ought not to have lost my temper.'

'You were quite right, though,' he returned harshly. 'It isn't any of my business.' And on that he added a brief 'Excuse me,' and strode away in the direction of the homestead.

Loretta was undecided about going down to dinner that evening, but after some consideration she felt she ought to do so if only because the table would be laid for her and Paul would have to make some excuse for her absence.

Having mistaken the time she was dismayed to find herself alone with Paul when she entered the sitting-room where aperitifs were to be served on the verandah.

'Has no one arrived yet?' She glanced around, then felt foolish for doing so. She expected a sarcastic rejoinder but instead Paul surprised her by commenting on her appearance.

'You look particularly charming tonight, Loretta.' His tawny eyes scanned her face before moving again to rove over her body. She felt stripped and lowered her head, hiding her rising colour. 'White suits you. Your dress is delightful.'

She glanced up then, bewildered that he should be so friendly after the harshness he had shown her just a short while ago.

'Thank you,' she said demurely.

'Come, let us have a drink before the others arrive.' He flicked a hand; she preceded him on to the verandah and he followed with the drinks.

She looked at him as he went to stand by the rail after handing her the glass. So distinguished and tall, with the kind of frame any athlete would wish to have. Not an ounce of surplus weight on those narrow hips or those sinewed limbs. And those hands. . . . From the first they had fascinated her with their slenderness, which she knew possessed a hidden strength that could hurt if their owner wished them to. His face was half turned from her so that his strong, classical profile was silhouetted against the falling darkness of the sky. But from behind the leaves of a vine lights from the house fell on to his face, accentuating the arrogance, the impression of superiority and mastery. Yes, he was special, she thought, vitally aware of his masculinity and of the fact that they were alone out here. There was no sound but that of the breeze rustling the palm fronds in the garden and the foliage of other trees upstream. It was a breeze which often came down from the mountains, passing through thousands of pine needles which sometimes produced soft, tenuous music, faintly weird. This evening she had to listen for it, separate it from the other sounds it made as it danced among the branches of the trees. Yes, she could just about pick it out . . . like the fluttering of wings, almost.

Lost in the magic of it all she was faintly vexed on hearing Paul say, a curious inflection in his voice, 'What are you thinking about, Loretta?' He had turned his head and was looking straight at her. 'You were a long way off, weren't you?'

She shook her head, unaware that the movement caught the light which in turn accentuated the glowing beauty of her hair. Unaware, too, that Paul was seeing a charming simplicity in her manner, yet a certain dignity in her poise. All she did know was that his eyes were intense as he waited for her to speak.

'I was listening to the breeze,' she confessed. 'It makes the sweetest music at times—' She broke off with a little self-conscious laugh. 'I expect that you, as a man, would consider that silly and—and romantic.' Again that awkwardness, that feeling of unease with which his godlike presence sometimes affected her.

'No, why should I consider it silly and romantic?'

'You surprise me,' she said.

'And you surprise me,' was his cryptic rejoinder. And then he moved over to a small rattan table, one of several scattered about the wide, flower-draped verandah—or *stoep*—and put down his glass. Loretta's nerves tingled for she felt again that electric current in the air around them. She wanted to shy away from him as he came closer and yet, paradoxi-

73

cally, she could have risen from her chair and gone eagerly into his arms even before he reached for her wrist and brought her to her feet.

His voice was low but commanding as he said, 'You're far too attractive tonight, Loretta. I am going to kiss you and you will not fight me, understand?'

She did not know what to say; feeling a protest was necessary but unable to voice it she merely looked up into his hard face and waited, nerves rioting, heart racing abnormally.

He bent his head, slowly. She felt the coolness of his breath on her cheek, the strength of his arms as they came about her, the touch of his lips which was the prelude to a long and masterful kiss. She felt his rippling muscles against her soft curves, the granite hardness of his arms as they spread down her spine then crushed her even closer to him. Her senses reeled and fire shot through her when his hands curved around her lower body. The musky male odour of him assailed her nostrils, awakening another sense as it blended with her own exotic perfume, just as their bodies were blending in movements that were all primitive, abandoned and savage. His mouth was in full possession of hers, his tongue rough and masterful in its exploration and its teasing. One lean brown hand found her breast and she gave a little gasp, managing to look up when for a moment his lips freed hers. In her eyes was a protest which never reached her lips, for, sensitized by the sheer magnificence of him, she saw him as an exalted being, far, far above her, a god whose power she dared not challenge or defy.

'Relax,' he ordered and she obeyed, allowing him to have his way with her—to caress her breasts, to tease the nipples one after the other until every nerve cell in her body was ignited by the torrid heat of his passion. She arched in supplication when his hands pressed more roughly and demandingly on her lower curves, and the rock hardness of his thighs, solid against her soft young body, hurt abominably, but she could not voice a protest. His mouth was on hers again, hard, demanding, almost brutal in its mastery as her lips were forced apart and she was made to reciprocate by mating her tongue with his.

'You're the most delightful creature I have ever met.' Paul's voice was a throaty bass tone against her ear. 'I ought to take you—I would if we hadn't these people coming.' So confident! Anger rose within her but was soon crushed under the deluge of his resumed love-making. Soon her pulses were drumming as his mouth teased the hollows of her throat, the tips of her ears, and then his rough tongue was on her nipple, swelling it again to the hard bud of desire. She was lost, she thought, and did not care. Life was for living and this was heaven with the final crowning glory of rapture no more than a breath away.

'Mr. Paul, the first guests are here.'

The voice of the houseboy. He stood at a very respectful distance and turned away as soon as Loretta and Paul had put space between them. Paul's voice staggered her by its calmness as he said, 'Thank you, Ngugi. Show them into the salon.'

* * *

75

Loretta could not take her eyes off Olga, who was sitting next to Paul, on his right. The girl was dazzlingly beautiful tonight, with a daringly low-cut evening dress of midnight blue organza trimmed with sequins and tiny pearls. She wore a diamond necklace and matching ear drops and bracelet. Loretta had learned that her father had made his money in industry but now owned a large citrus estate similiar to that of Paul. And as Olga was the only child she obviously basked in wealth and it was plain to see that she could have everything she wanted.

Everything. . . . She wanted Paul, but did he want her? He was not averse to a flirtation with another girl. Loretta frowned at the word, for while she knew that on Paul's part it must be a flirtation, she herself was fast falling in love with him. Yes, it was useless to deny it, but while she was admitting this she was at the same time thinking of Lee and his unhappiness. He loved her dearly, while Paul probably loved Olga—or even if he did not love her it would seem that there was every possibility of his marrying her. Perhaps he was interested in joining the two estates, since they were not too far away from one another and all that separated them was a few miles of unproductive bushveld which in all probability Paul could buy.

'Just when are you two going to invite us to a wedding?' The voice of Garth Helmley brought Loretta from her reverie with a start. She felt her heart lurch as she glanced up the table to where Paul and Olga were sitting. She had been miles away and had missed whatever had led up to Garth's question. He was the proprietor of the warehouse where agricultural implements could be bought and Loretta had been introduced to him when she and Paul had dined once at the Acacia Club. Olga had been away on a brief visit to her mother, from whom her father was divorced, and so she was not present. Garth had joined them, as he was alone, but now Edna, his very new girl-friend, was with him. Edna had come as nanny to the three children of Mary and James Baker, who ran the Acacia Club.

'Yes, Paul,' from Mary with a light laugh, 'we all guess it won't be long, but when?'

Paul's face was a study as silence fell. Olga was staring right into Loretta's eyes, malice and triumph mingling in her gaze.

'Neither Olga nor I have discussed anything about marriage,' said Paul with a sort of mild politeness. 'I am not so sure that Olga wants to be saddled with a man like me,' he added and it was plain to Loretta, if to no one else, that his good humour was forced. He was angry, furiously so, for being put on the spot like that. Garth was colouring up, aware he had been exceedingly untactful. Mary, too, had subsided into silence, toying with her food and doubtless feeling almost as uncomfortable as Garth.

Loretta met Olga's gaze again and this time there was unmistakable fury in the depths of her eyes.

What was Paul's intention? The question was still with Loretta when, the dinner party over, she once more found herself alone with Paul. She just had to say, in a husky little voice, 'Olga was very lovely tonight. It's—it's no wonder you—you—er—like her.'

If she believed she'd been subtle then she was very soon disillusioned as Paul said, with a hint of sardonic amusement, 'What exactly are you asking me, Loretta?'

'Nothing,' swiftly and with a shake of her head. 'I don't know what you mean.'

'You'd like to know if Olga and I will eventually get married?'

'You once said you might get married. You said a man wants an heir.'

'Did I? My memory is not too good these days.'

'I wish I could understand you!'

'You might, if you tried,' was his veiled rejoinder.

'You seem to delight in baffling me!'

The straight dark brows lifted a fraction. 'Is there any particular reason why I should put you in possession of knowledge that concerns me alone?'

Blushing at his arrogance she spoke in no more than a whisper. 'No—I'm sorry. After all, we're strangers, aren't we? I mean—I've only been here two and a half weeks.'

'Strangers?' A low laugh escaped him and before she knew what he was about she found herself captured in arms as strong as tempered steel and her mouth was crushed unmercifully.

'Let me go!' she cried when eventually she had the chance to speak. 'I told you I'm not interested in flirtations!'

'But you enjoy my amorous exploits all the same.' He was mocking her, thoroughly satisfied by his ability to force her to surrender. 'Be honest with yourself, little one, and admit that you're a very sexy young lady.'

'Oh, I hate you!' Without thinking she lashed out at his cheek, then looked with horror at the tiny streak of blood oozing from the wound inflicted by her fingernail. A quivering hand went to her own cheek as she murmured contritely, every vestige of anger gone, 'I'm sorry—I didn't mean—to do that. You—shouldn't have goaded me,' she ended on a little note of defiance.

He stood towering above her, a menacing figure with the sort of glint in his eyes that made Loretta tremble in her shoes.

'I ought to throw you across my knee for that,' he said at last in a dangerously quiet tone of voice. 'I feel like making you smart for a week!'

She caught her underlip between her teeth, aware that she was trembling, but dared not move in case she should add fuel to his anger and earn herself the beating he was half promising her.

'I'm very sorry,' she murmured again. 'I didn't mean to—to draw blood. . . . She tailed off, aware of her mistake, but unable to rectify it. Paul had not known she had drawn blood and now, as he put up a hand to touch the place where she had slapped him, she watched with dilated eyes and managed to take a step backwards, towards the half-open door. He gazed at the blood on his finger then transferred his attention to Loretta. 'You—you shouldn't h-have goaded me,' she said again and took another step nearer the door.

'You little vixen,' he said in a very soft voice. 'Yes,

my girl, I ought to tan that hide of yours so hard you'd not sit down for a month. As it is—off you go before I change my mind.' But, as if he just could not completely hold his temper in check, he moved across the room and as Loretta fled in alarm he gave her a resounding slap that made her wince. Instinctively she swung around.

'Why, you—!'

'Are you going to take my advice?' he asked her gently, 'or do you intend to push your luck a little further?'

She glared at him, opened her mouth to make a retort, then changed her mind and left, tears of mortification blinding her vision as she made her way to her room.

Chapter Five

After a restless night Loretta awoke to the sun pouring into her room and only now did she realise she had not drawn the curtains last night when she came into her bedroom. Memory flooded in and she blushed at the way Paul had treated her. How dared he strike her! Yet she had struck him first. Suddenly it struck Loretta that the whole situation between her and Paul was far too familiar. Why, they were almost like a married couple in the way they acted towards one another. She had to smile at that, for surely married couples did not strike one another in the way she and Paul had done . . . or did they? She had been goaded, but then so had Paul. Again she saw him standing there after she had hit him, tall and towering and very angry, with that red mark so incongruous on a face as noble and arrogant as Paul's. If he had carried out his threat she was honest enough to own that she could hardly have blamed him, for it must have been more than a little humiliating for him to be treated like that.

She slid from beneath the sheet and went to the bathroom, where she took a shower and tried to dismiss last night's humiliating experience from her mind. She would go and spend the whole day at Lee's house, doing various chores and cooking him a meal ready for when he arrived home. She could persuade him to finish early, and in any case he always went back to his house for lunch. This was one advantage of working so close to one's home.

She went down to breakfast hoping Paul would already have had his but she was disappointed for he had waited for her.

'I'm sorry I'm late,' she felt obliged to say as she took possession of the chair he was holding out for her.

'Overslept after lying awake for hours,' he remarked perceptively. 'You should not be so eager to show those fangs—'

'Can we forget last night?' she broke in coldly. 'We both lost our tempers and for my part I would much rather put it right out of my mind.'

'Careful,' he warned, tawny eyes glinting. 'I could still give you that spanking I promised last night.'

'You're far too familiar,' she protested. 'I came here as your guest but you seem to have forgotten that I ought to be treated with respect.'

'Did you treat me with respect last night when you did this?' He indicated the very small clot that covered the wound.

'I've already admitted to losing my temper. I have

also apologised, several times—which is more than you have done!' she couldn't help adding.

'Nor do I intend to,' was his haughty response. 'On the contrary, I shall probably give you another rap on the behind before very long.'

She coloured and averted her head. How was she to deal with a man like this? Of course, she could leave his house, but where would she go? To Lee's? No, she still had an aversion to living alone with him, for tongues were sure to wag. Besides, what would Paul have to say—? She broke her thoughts, anger rising like a floodtide within her. What the devil had her actions to do with him anyway? And why was she so timid as to care, and to feel afraid of his reaction? It was almost as if he held some authority over her, as if he had her completely subjugated like some underling woman from the East where the man is undisputed master over all his womenfolk, from his sister to his wife.

'What the dickens are you thinking about to make you red in the face like that?' Paul's inquiry brought her back and she bit her lip in vexation at having allowed her musings to show on her face.

'You,' she retorted briefly, because that was the only answer she could conjure up for the moment.

'Me?' Paul's eyes widened. 'Do I cause you so much deep emotion?'

'Shut up!' she flashed and received a sharp rap on the knuckles from the back of the knife he was holding. She stared disbelievingly and got up from the table. Paul was beside her instantly and he ordered her to sit down again. 'I shall not! And I'm leaving here—!'

'Sit down,' softly but dangerously and Loretta felt tears of anger at the backs of her eyes.

'You can't make me,' she began, but already the pressure of his hand was on her shoulder and she was forced back on to the chair.

'Eat your breakfast.'

'I'm n-not hungry.'

'Eat it just the same.' He seemed indifferent all at once as, taking a piece of toast from the rack he began buttering it. Loretta eyed him warily, saw his eyes scarcely move, but in them was a glint which made her decide to capitulate. She ate more than she would have believed because she felt her appetite had been taken away.

'What are your plans for today?' he inquired when they had both finished and ready to leave the table.

'I'm spending the day at Lee's house. I can find some jobs to do.'

'I see,' tautly and with a compression of his mouth. 'Well, I shall expect you to be here for dinner.'

She sent him a sparkling glance. 'Oh, and why?'

'Because you owe it to me as my guest to dine with me.'

What an answer!

'You're used to dining alone, so why want company all at once?'

'I've become used to company.'

'Lee will expect me to stay late.'

'Then he's in for a disappointment.'

What was this all about? Was it her imagination or could it really be that Paul hated the idea of her staying late in Lee's home, alone with him in what would be a romantic setting, for it was most likely they'd be on the *stoep,* with flower scents in the air and the starlit sky above?

'I won't be dictated to, Paul,' she told him quietly. 'I am very conscious of being a guest of yours and I'm grateful that you've had me, but I can't allow you to run my life.'

He stared down at her with an intent gaze, his jawline hard, his eyes cold and narrowed. 'You'd not like Lee to get the sack, would you, Loretta?' he said and she gave an audible gasp.

'You wouldn't be so mean!'

'Don't try me,' he warned but she noticed that he was not looking at her.

'So you *are* dictating to me?'

'I am inviting you to have dinner with me.'

She drew an exasperated breath. 'Very well,' she conceded, 'I'll be back,' and she added tartly, 'What time would you like me? I wouldn't want to keep you waiting.'

'You know what time we dine.' The very quietness of his voice was a snub; she bit her lip and turned away. Paul rose and she followed, relieved to get out of the room and away from Paul's domineering presence. Yet she felt unconscionably depressed when, a few minutes later, she was walking slowly in the direction of Lee's homestead.

Lee was ready to go out. He was supervising the clearing of virgin bushveld, as Paul wanted to extend his orchards.

'I'd hoped you'd get here before I left,' he said, as he had already been aware that she was coming. 'Don't work too hard, will you?'

She smiled at him winningly, little realising that he saw again the girl she had been, the innocent eighteen-year-old who was desperately in love with him.

'You have the place so nice that I shall have to make work, I'm thinking.'

He looked at her tenderly. 'I wish you were to be here all the time, darling.'

'It isn't possible. Please don't ask me, Lee. I shall give you my decision in my own good time.'

She accompanied him to the door, thinking he looked very well in the khaki shorts and white short-sleeved shirt, with a slouch hat covering the grey of his hair. A surge of affection swelled within her as she lifted her face for his kiss.

'I love you so,' he whispered hoarsely. 'Try and love me as you used to, dearest.'

She stood on the step, her gaze following his figure along the narrow path, her mind confused, so much so that any chance of clear thought was impossible. So lonely he seemed as he walked along, not very quickly, as if he would not hurry the distance between them. He turned as she knew he would, and they waved to one another until he turned again and was lost to sight.

What was to be the end of it all? No use asking a question like that since an answer could not possibly present itself. She was more than half in love with Paul, who might or might not marry Olga. But in any case he would never love her, Loretta, for hadn't he owned that what was between him and her was nothing more than a flirtation? He liked making love to her, so she must attract him physically. That was not love and, as far as she could see, never would be. Olga was there, with her beauty and her poise and her great wealth, so what chance had Loretta against her?

With a sigh she went into the kitchen and began to take down pots and jars and jugs from the shelves, for she had already noticed that although all was neat, the shelves had not been scrubbed for a very long time. This task took her until eleven o'clock and she decided to make herself a cup of tea and have it on the shady *stoep*. She had donned a dark blue nylon overall and had rolled up the sleeves to above the elbows. She had just taken out her tea when she saw Olga sauntering along the wide path towards Rikuyu Lodge. She made to draw back before the girl caught sight of her but was too late. Olga pulled up abruptly, then came on down the narrower path leading to Lee's house.

Frowning, Loretta stood there, waiting, and wondering what the girl wanted with her. There was arrogance in everything about her—the way she walked and held her head, the length of her steps, even the way she swung her arms. She slowed as she drew nearer and her eyes swept Loretta's figure disdainfully. Cursing herself for not disappearing into the house and taking off the overall, which was soiled now and splashed with water, Loretta had no option but to stand there and resign herself to being examined in this contemptuous way. She wondered what Paul saw in the girl, for surely he looked below that beautiful veneer?

'Hello, there. You look as if you're Lee's house-girl.' Olga glanced at the cup of tea. 'Mid-morning break, I see.'

Loretta's chin lifted. 'Did you want Lee?' she inquired coldly.

'Lee?' with a widening gaze and a curl of the lips. 'What on earth would I want with Lee—a servant of my fiancé?'

Angry colour leapt to Loretta's cheeks. But she made no reference to Olga's nasty remark about Lee as she said, 'I didn't know that you and Paul were engaged. It didn't sound like it last night,' she just had to add, feeling catty all at once.

Faint colour only served to enhance the beauty of Olga's face. 'Paul was evasive, I admit, but he's like that—resents anyone asking questions.'

Loretta let that pass without further comment. 'Why are you here, Olga?' she asked.

'It's just a friendly call—I noticed you here and thought I'd have a few words.'

Loretta lifted her eyebrows and said, 'Your approach was far from friendly. You likened me to a housegirl.'

'Owing to that—er—garment you are wearing.' The sneer in her voice matched the contemptuous expression in her eyes.

'You're about the rudest person I have ever met!'

Olga gave a slight start; it was clear that she had not expected anything quite as outspoken as that. 'I

88

think I had better leave. I wonder what Paul will have to say when I tell him you insulted me.'

'Shall you explain that you asked for it by insulting me first?' inquired Loretta, adopting an air of acid sweetness.

'You're impertinent!'

'I'd still like to know what brought you here.' Loretta looked curiously at her but Olga seemed at a loss for words. 'You don't know yourself, do you? You saw me and on impulse came along, not knowing why.'

A sneer caught the older girl's underlip. 'You seem to think you know everything!'

'I'm not totally obtuse.'

'I suppose,' said Olga changing her manner with startling suddenness, 'that I was curious as to why you're here. I know you're a friend of Lee, but that was as much as Paul would tell me.'

'And so you thought you'd come along and question me?' Loretta was remembering her impression recently that the girl might be jealous of her presence in Paul's home.

'I feel it's strange that you should have come all this way to visit a married man.'

Loretta had to smile at the girl's undisguised curiosity. 'Paul knows all about it,' she said, 'so if you want more information I suggest you ask him. After all,' she was impelled to add, driven on by some imp of mischief, 'you and he are engaged, you say, so obviously there'll not be any secrets between you, will there?'

Olga's mouth went tight and her hands were

clenched at her sides. The colour was fading from her face, too, as if she were straining to control a fury which was fast rising within her. 'I think I had better go,' she said again, and without another word she swung around and began walking swiftly back to the wider path.

Loretta sighed and shook her head, her brow creased in thought. Just how close were those two to being engaged? she wondered. Surely Olga would never have spoken like that unless she was sure of her position. Loretta sat down on the *stoep* and picked up her tea. It had gone cold but she drank it all the same. Ought she to stay here? She now felt sure that seeing those two married would be unendurable. Also, she could not envisage herself as Lee's wife even were he free. Yet at the same time she could not bear the thought of leaving him now that they had met again. She had awakened all his love by this visit, had given him hope without actually realising it—yes, he was hoping for something permanent to come from this visit, hoping she would eventually become his wife. She would be loved, she had no doubts about that, dearly loved and cherished . . . like a daughter who had to be tenderly nurtured. . . .

Another sigh escaped her and she stood up, feeling all at sixes and sevens, suddenly desirous of escape, although in what form she had no idea. All she knew was that things were getting on top of her, becoming a burden she felt she could not much longer carry. Regret at coming was deep within her; she hated fate because it was fate that had shaped everything, from the moment she had met Lee, so much older than herself, to his leaving her and then the lost letter which caused the long separation. Fate again planned her visit to the village and to the post office where she found Lee's long lost proposal of marriage, for that was in effect what his letter meant. Then her aunt's legacy, but for which she could not have made this trip, a trip which she felt would shape her life in a way she had never ever contemplated— She broke her train of thought because by now she *was* seeing herself as Lee's wife. . . .

'I can't hurt him by leaving him!' she cried, misery sweeping over her like a deluge. 'Yet how can I marry him when I don't love him?'

She had to get away from his house and with speed she discarded the overall, washed her hands and face and went out along the path to where it joined that leading to Paul's house. Suddenly she felt free, as if she had shed the burden . . . but she knew it was a transient sensation that would pass. The burden could not be thrown off so lightly as that.

Paul and Olga were in the garden of Rikuyu Lodge, sitting on a bench beneath a spreading baobab tree. They both glanced up as she approached the house and Paul said, 'Back already? I thought you were spending the day over at Lee's place?' His gaze was curious, all-examining; she felt sure he could read her mind, so astute was he at times.

'I've done some work,' she replied lamely.

'And now?'

'She wants a rest, darling,' from Olga in purring

tones which reminded Loretta of an animal with claws. 'When I was over there Miss Sedgewick looked positively worn out.'

Loretta cast her a darkling glance and, entirely because Paul was there, she said spitefully, 'And I looked like a housegirl, you said, remember?'

Silence, long and profound. Loretta could not bear it so she calmly walked away, her cheeks red because of what she had done. She was furious with herself, but that girl brought out the worst in her!

She continued to stroll across the broad expanse of Paul's garden, glad when she was out of sight of the two whom she surmised were following her with their eyes. It had rained in the night—in fact there had been a storm—and the air was fresh and cool above earth that had come to life as the dust was laid. The sun's rays were golden, painting the summits of the mountains and the foothills below them. She glanced at the homestead, bright in the sunlight, an elegant home with shady *stoeps* at each side of the imposing, white-pillared entrance. An abundance of flowering trees and shrubs lent glorious colour to supplement the verdant green of the perfectly-manicured lawns. She stopped now and then to admire a bed of canna lilies or lovely golden allamandas. Roses abounded and passion flowers, while all along one side of the path she had begun to take was a glorious hedge of crimson hibiscus while on the other side a tall oleander hedge contrasted with it, its milky white blossoms glowing and moving as the zephyr of a breeze drifted through them. She had gone some distance along the riverbed when she became tense, aware of another presence, and she swung round, the fine golden hairs rising on her forearms.

'Oh, you frightened me!' she exclaimed, angry because of her fear.

'I'm sorry. I thought I was making myself heard.'

He stopped as he reached her and she stared up into the bronzed, handsome face.

'I didn't hear you.' She looked past him, expecting to see Olga, and then realised that if the girl had accompanied him she would scarcely be lagging behind. 'Why—why are you here?' she had to ask, for it did seem strange that he should be following her. 'Surely you are not out for a stroll as well?'

'I came after you.' Flexed the jaw and crisp the tone. 'What was wrong between you and Olga?'

'It doesn't matter, Paul—' She shrugged her shoulders in a careless gesture. 'She and I could never get along in a million years.'

Paul leant against a tree and thrust his hands into his pockets. 'Is there any reason why you should?'

She frowned at him. 'That's a strange thing to say, isn't it?' She paused, but he made no answer; he was searching her face as if attempting to discover something from her expression and she knew he was exceedingly curious as to what had transpired between her and his girl-friend a short while ago. 'While I'm a guest in your house I ought to be able to get along with your—fiancée, shouldn't I?' She was being deliberately catty but she was only human after all, she told herself by way of an excuse.

'Fiancée?' with a faintly sardonic lift of his brows. 'You know very well that Olga and I aren't engaged.'

'She said you were.'

The tawny eyes narrowed perceptively and his lips twitched with amusement. 'So my little one has claws of a different kind, has she?' And he deliberately fingered the tiny scar she had made last night. She went red, as he meant her to, but she sent him a speaking look as her back stiffened and her pointed little chin lifted.

'I spoke only the truth,' she snapped.

'But to let me know that Olga had been telling fibs.'

Loretta turned her back to him, to stare at a gaudily-plumaged bird chirping merrily on the low branch of a gum tree. Two very dark brown butterflies were fluttering their delicate wings above some bright magenta flowers growing low beneath the bushes scattered along the river bank, and a little green lizard darted about close to her feet, catching flies. So silent it all was! Like time standing still, smothered in the hush of eternity. Something quivered through her body, because she felt so close to nature, part of it, and of this dark and primitive land whose mysteries still puzzled and enthralled men even today. She heard the quiet voice behind her, quiet, yes, but commanding, as if its owner had some authority over her.

'Turn around, Loretta.'

She obeyed without knowing why, and looked up into his finely-chiselled features. He seemed so stern and implacable, so out of her reach.

'What is it?' That familiar awkwardness was slowly creeping over her and she had the urge to turn away again but something in that stern countenance kept her where she was.

'Loretta,' he said quietly, 'what are your intentions regarding Lee?'

The question, so unexpected, startled her and she looked at him without speaking for fully twenty seconds. 'Why should you be interested?' she queried at last.

'I have my reasons.' A small pause and then, 'I feel responsible for you, I suppose, since you're my guest.'

'That wasn't the reason for your question.'

He smiled then and said, 'No, little one, it was not the reason. However, since I am not intending to give you the real reason the one I offered will suffice. Tell me, are you seriously thinking of partnering up with him?' Tense the tone now and a muscle rioted in his cheek, moving the scar she had inflicted.

'Partnering?' she echoed, feigning ignorance.

'You have my meaning,' tautly and faintly admonishing. 'So don't pretend. You know as well as I that you can't marry Lee, and if you want to go to him it will have to be as his mistress—' He stopped abruptly and a scowl darkened his face. Loretta's eyes narrowed with perception.

'You obviously don't care for the idea?' She was watching him intently, the most incredible idea crossing her mind. Paul *hated* to mention the word 'mistress' in connection with her!

What did that mean? Did he like her a little . . . or a lot . . . ? He had been rather emphatic in telling her just now that he and Olga weren't engaged. And those kisses and that almost savage love-making? He had intimated it was a mere flirtation but looking at it now it seemed very odd for him to be making love

to her if he intended marrying Olga. . . . Nerves
quivered and her heart began to beat over-rate at
the possibility that he could care for her in that
way.

And suddenly she knew she loved him, wildly,
passionately. She had owned to being half way there
but she now realised her reluctance to allow her
feelings full sway; she had subconsciously believed
she could protect her heart by a sort of stubborn
refusal to allow the full meaning of what she felt for
Paul to take possession of her mind.

But now revelation was with her and nothing
could erase it. From this moment on she could not
refuse to accept what was a fact.

'I feel you would be throwing yourself away.'
Paul's voice broke into her thoughts and she looked
up again into his face. It was a mask, inscrutable.
'Lee is far too old for you, and added to that he is
married.'

She passed a tongue over lips that seemed suddenly to have become dry and parched. How could she
discover what Paul's feelings towards her were? That
he was anxious was plain, for otherwise he would not
be here now, talking about Lee and what would
happen to her should she decide to throw in her lot
with him.

Anxious, yes, but anything else?

She said, her voice low and faintly hollow, 'Lee
and I haven't yet come to any conclusion about our
future together.'

A silence ensued. He seemed grimly distant and
yet she had the impression that a confession hovered
on his lips.

'Loretta,' he said at last, his eyes never leaving her face, 'will you promise me one thing?'

'Yes—of course.' Her limpid gaze was fixed, her mouth softly parted as for one intensely profound moment a deep hush lay between them, an intimate silence like time balancing in total equilibrium. 'Yes, Paul, I will make the promise you ask of me.' Her voice was low and sweet, her small hands together as if in unconscious prayer. Paul seemed almost spellbound and she half expected him to take her in his arms, to kiss her with a tenderness he had never shown before.

Instead, he said softly, 'Promise me, little one, that you will never allow pity to influence your decision.'

'Pity?' Yes, she knew an overwhelming pity for Lee, who was nearing fifty and was unhappy and very lonely . . . with no future if she were to decide not to marry him. She found it difficult to make the promise even though she had assured Paul she would make it. 'I do pity him,' she murmured, feeling suddenly distraught. 'What has he in his life, Paul?'

'Life is unpredictable, Loretta, as is one's future. But each one of us is given a life and it's our very own to do with it what we like—'

'Fate interferes, though!'

'I must agree.' He looked at her intently and for a long moment before adding, 'You believe that your life has been influenced by fate, don't you?'

'I know it has. Why am I here now?'

He nodded musingly. 'Yet it won't be anything to do with fate if you allow pity to dictate in your relationship with Lee.'

'If I had received that letter then I'd be married to him now; we'd have children and he'd be a happy man.'

'But would you be a happy woman?' He paused to survey her critically. 'Our lives are not for sacrificing,' he went on gravely. 'There are those who would argue with me about that, and there are those who might consider me selfish. But in my opinion the only sacrifices we should make should be for those we love.'

So serious and so gentle, somehow, his whole manner. She stared up into his face with a sort of uncomprehending wonderment, for this was a very different man from the Paul she had known up till now.

'Why are you so concerned about me?' she found herself asking.

'I just don't want a lovely girl like you sacrificing her life for someone she does not love.'

'You've always been so sure I don't love Lee.'

'Do you?' Brief the question and one she had to answer truthfully.

'No, Paul, I don't love him.'

'Then make me the promise.'

But she shook her head, eyes apologetic. 'I can't, Paul—I just can't!' What had made her say that? She surely knew she could never marry Lee now that she had discovered she loved Paul. But Paul might be out of her reach—she felt sure he was for, if he cared, why, then, did he not tell her so? But even as she was asking this she at the same time admitted that Paul was a reserved man who, she felt sure, would never reveal his feelings without a great deal of prior thought.

But if only he would give her a clue. . . .

Wishful thinking? She suddenly realised she had been half assuming something for which there was no real foundation. Paul was anxious about her and that was all, she firmly assured herself, and decided not to allow the matter to trouble her again.

'Make me the promise!' Imperious the words and demanding in the way they were delivered. 'You said you would—and I'm waiting!'

She shook her head, but weakly. He was far too overpowering, too able in the way he made her feel small and obliged to do his bidding. 'I can't—please—'

'You can and you will!' Without giving her the chance to speak he had reached out to grip her wrist; she was jerked almost roughly to his hard body; her head was brought up by the simple expedient of his grabbing a handful of hair and tugging it, with total unconcern for the little cry of protest and pain it brought from her trembling lips. 'You will, I say!' His mouth possessed hers, crushing it beneath his own moist and parted lips. She tried to struggle but his arms were strong as tempered steel about her and she gave up. In any case, he meant to force surrender and, as a result, reciprocation. She felt the prick of tears as his hard body hurt her, knew her mouth was being bruised, but she could do nothing to stem the torrent of his ardour as he took her breast, almost tearing away the buttons when he forced his hand inside her blouse. He brought her breast to his lips, teasing the nipple with his tongue until she felt the blood hot in her veins as desire tore at her nerves, compelling her to arch against his hard male virility in spasmodic movements which melded erotically with his own. 'Promise!' he ordered, his cool, sensuous mouth caressing the delicate hollow of her throat. 'Obey me, Loretta . . . or else. . . .'

'It's—it's coercion—'

'Call it what you like but you'll do as I tell you!'

'Paul—let me go!'

He shook her, then brought her roughly to his rock-hard frame again. She was still in the torrid throes of passion, craving for fulfilment, and with a little strangled cry of resignation she gave him the promise he was so forcefully demanding of her.

Chapter Six

It was half-past five when Lee arrived home to find an appetising meal ready for him.

'Aren't you having anything—?' He looked at Loretta, a puzzled frown on his face.

'Paul wants me to have dinner with him.' She had almost used the word 'insisted,' then managed to hold it back. 'You see, he feels I owe it to him, being a guest in his house.' She was remembering with profound intensity the scene by the riverbed when he had forced the promise from her, the promise that she would not allow pity to influence her decision as regards Lee.

'That seems rather strange.' Lee's frown deepened. 'He knows very well that you came specifically to see me and that it's only because of convention that you're staying in his house.'

She gave a loud sigh. 'I shall have to go, Lee—I'm

so sorry.' She felt rotten, and because of it misery flooded over her. She wanted to cry for his loneliness. Here she had made him a tempting meal and was not staying to share it. No wonder he considered it all wrong.

'Paul has no right to demand this of you,' declared Lee angrily. 'I shall have a word with him about it!'

She made no answer, for she felt choked as she looked at him, standing there, a frown creasing his brow and in his eyes that look of sadness not unmingled with bewilderment. 'Didn't you tell him you preferred to have dinner with me?'

'I tried to tell him that I ought to be with you, but—but he—he seemed to feel that I ought to dine with him. . . .' She tailed off lamely, unhappily aware that this was no explanation at all.

'Loretta, can it be that you would rather be with Paul?' He subjected her to a keen and searching scrutiny. 'He's a most attractive man, and he's seventeen years younger than I—'

'Oh, don't!' she cried. And then, as if the words were drawn from her through compassion, 'What has age to do with it?'

'A great deal, my dear. It was the difference in our ages which brought about the separation in the first place.'

'You went away from me! You'd no need to have gone!'

'Your mother resented me; she told me I was old enough to be your father. Our association was upsetting to her.' He paused, watching her as she stood by the daintily-laid table, one hand resting on the snow-white cloth, the other tightly closed at her side. She was trembling, not visibly, but he seemed to know. His eyes moved from the unnatural pallor of her face to the delicate curve of her throat, and his mouth moved convulsively. 'I went, dear, because to me at that time it was the honourable thing to do. I wanted to give you time on your own to consider, to see the future when you'd be a mother whose children would have a father old enough to be their grandfather— No, don't interrupt, Loretta, for what I'm saying is true. Your mother pointed this out, too, and so I came to the reluctant conclusion that I must go away in order to give you breathing space, as it were.' He paused in hesitation as if considering carefully his next words. 'I just had to send the letter in the end. I loved you so deeply I felt I could not face life without you no matter what the future might bring. I felt a cad for writing, darling, but I had to.' He put his face in his hands and in horror she ran to him, sure he was crying.

'Oh, dearest Lee—don't! Please, darling—there is no need for you to be so upset! I—I love you. . . .' The words had left her lips unknowingly in her urgency to assuage his misery and although she would have drawn them back if she could she still held him to her protectively, her hand at the back of his head, her cheek touching his. 'Lee, don't be sad,' she pleaded. 'To see you like this hurts me—here!' Automatically she put a hand to her heart, inserting it between their bodies. He moved, to hold her from him and looked deeply, searchingly, into her eyes.

'You said you love me, darling. You meant it, because I know you'd never lie. Oh, sweet, you've made me happy.' Surreptitiously he brushed a hand across his eyes. 'Tomorrow, dear, we shall talk, but for now I know you must be hurrying away. Tomorrow evening we shall go to the Club and celebrate—'

'Lee, I—'

'I have the day off, so be early, love, as early as you can.'

God, what had she done? she was asking herself as she hurried along the narrow path, knowing she must soon turn and wave to Lee who would be standing there, waiting, a happy man. . . . 'I hate myself! And yet, what could I do? His misery was crucifying me!'

She turned and lifted a trembling hand. Lee, even from this distance, seemed to have shed a great burden . . . and it was all due to her.

Paul was in the sitting-room when she came down, dressed in a dainty trouser suit which at first she had been doubtful about wearing in case he should not approve. Then she was angrily asking herself why she should care whether he approved or not. She had more on her mind than the trivial anxiety as to his opinion of her attire.

He looked her over and said to her surprise, 'I like it. You have the figure for pants—which so many women have not.' He was in a casual suit of oyster-coloured linen with a white shirt beneath the blouson-type jacket; his hair shone as usual and his tan seemed deeper than ever. A man of the great outdoors, tall and sinewed and young. . . . 'Sit down, little one, and I'll get you a drink.' He walked away, taking a couple of graceful strides to bring him to the drinks cabinet. Loretta watched with dulled eyes, her whole mind having returned to Lee, who was dining alone, and in her compassionate heart she was saying, 'Oh, God, I can't bear it—can't bear to think of his loneliness!'

Paul had turned, stopping abruptly in his tracks, a frown swiftly darkening his brow. 'What on earth's wrong, Loretta? You look devastated.'

She swallowed; tears were close, so what use was it to try to smile? And yet she did, but it was a weak attempt which had no effect in deceiving Paul any more than the feigned lightness of her voice when she spoke. 'I hope I don't look devastated! I feel fine!'

Paul's eyes narrowed; he advanced slowly towards her, two glasses in his hands. 'You've recently come from Lee's house. I saw you about an hour or so ago coming along the path. What's wrong with you?' he said again, then added sharply, 'Don't try to deceive me, Loretta. I *am* possessed of a modicum of perception, you know.'

She bit her lip, hesitating because, although she wanted to confide, there was no doubt at all that she would make him angry. She did speak at last, though, opening her heart after all, because she was weighed down with misery and uncertainty, her soft heart telling her she ought to go to Lee even though she knew she could never love him.

'Lee's so lonely, and I was upset at leaving him. I—I said I l—' She stopped, but then went on, avoiding Paul's dark and piercing gaze. 'It came out, Paul and I couldn't help it! I told him I loved him— Oh, please don't look like that! It has nothing to do with you, after all.' She was crying suddenly because

105

he was so angry and because she sought comfort where none was available. He just stood there in a magisterial attitude, subjecting her to a dark and censorious scrutiny, and as the moments stretched she felt she wanted to scream in order to relieve her feelings.

'You lied to him, just because you were sorry for him?' So hard the tone, inflexible, and as condemning as the expression in his eyes.

'He was so lost—it was because I wasn't staying to dinner. He couldn't understand why I should be here instead of with him. Oh, Paul, you have no idea how unhappy he looked! I had to do something when—when he started to cry, so I held him close and t-told him I l-loved him.' The tears flowed but seemed to have no effect on the stern and disapproving man standing there, as if in judgement on her.

When he spoke it was to say, with a hint of derision in his voice, 'He cried, you say—actually shed tears?'

Her chin went up. 'Why shouldn't a man cry!'

'You obviously didn't like it.' Paul moved to place her drink on a table at her elbow.

'Because it upset me to see a man cry. It meant that Lee must have been right down in the depths of despair.'

'Have you considered what his position has been for the past year, ever since his wife decided to leave him? He's been on his own, and he appeared quite all right to me.'

'But now he's met me again— Oh, I wish I'd never come! That letter—why did it have to turn up after all that time? And why did Auntie have to die and leave me money to come here?'

'I believe you blame fate.'

'You're totally without feeling!'

'Because I don't take out a handkerchief and dry your eyes?'

'I'd not want you to do that!' But it was just what she did want him to do, and then take her in his arms and attempt to soothe away her misery. 'You're cold and unfeeling and—and I hate you!'

'Hate?' Faintly he smiled in a most peculiar kind of way, a slanting smile and knowledgeable. 'I think not, my little one. No, I am very sure you don't hate me.'

Her eyes flew to his, to regard him through a mist of tears.

'Well,' she amended, 'I dislike you intensely.'

'Have you forgotten you're a guest in my house?' he asked her softly. 'It isn't polite to tell your host you dislike him.'

'You and I seem to be more than host and guest,' she found herself saying. 'It has been like that right from the start.'

'*What* has it been like?'

'Well . . . the way you've acted, not—' She broke off, blushing at the memories of his passionate love-making.

'As a host should?' with a reappearance of that slanting smile, though this time it portrayed only amusement. 'Nor have you acted as any demure guest should.' He lifted his glass to take a sip of his sherry. 'Shall we get back to this business of Lee?'

he suggested after producing a handkerchief from his jacket pocket and dropping it on to her lap. 'You're going to have to tell him that you lied, having been carried away by pity.'

'I could never do that.' She shook her head vigorously. 'It would be cruel to hurt him so.'

'Then tell me, what *are* your intentions?' His voice had changed and was now as sharp as steel, as was the expression in those tawny eyes.

'I haven't had time to think. All I know is that I cannot hurt him—no, it would be impossible.' She dabbed her eyes, then blew her nose and held up the handkerchief which he accepted gingerly and put back into his pocket.

'So you have already forgotten your promise to me?'

'I can't think why you asked for it,' she responded in a tone of complaint. 'Anyway, I can't keep it—at least, I am going to forget I ever made it.'

'By God, you are not!' The sudden, unexpected violence of his words made her jump visibly and the wine spilled on to her pants. With a frown Paul produced the handkerchief again and attempted to remove the stain.

'It doesn't matter,' she said and drew away.

'You shall not forget that promise,' he insisted, almost glowering at her, a circumstance which bewildered her and yet brought to mind with stark clarity her previous idea that Paul might be finding her attractive. But at this moment it certainly did not seem as if he were finding her attractive, as his expression changed and his eyes were filled with contempt. 'Promises are not made to be broken lightly, my girl, and just you remember that.'

More bewildered than ever, she could only stare for a long moment in silence, watching the anger on his face and the darkling look in his eyes.

'It has nothing to do with you,' she said again, but weakly this time, for he was altogether too overpowering, too big and domineering, while she felt small and drained and very tired.

'I want to go to my room,' she began. 'I'm not fit to be anyone's companion at the dinner table.'

She half rose as she spoke but as she put her glass down Paul said, his anger miraculously disappearing, 'Sit down, Loretta; I'm not allowing you to be alone while you're in this distressed state.'

'I wish I understood you,' she complained, sitting down again. 'One moment you're angry with me and the next you're anxious about me.'

The shadow of a smile crossed his face. 'You will understand me soon enough,' he returned cryptically. 'For the present, though . . .' His voice became softer as he continued, 'I want you to keep in mind that I am seriously concerned about you, and secondly that I expect you to keep the promise you made me.'

'Paul—I—' She was stopped by an imperious lift of his hand.

'We shall let the matter drop for this evening, Loretta, and enjoy our meal. There's always another day tomorrow, and after a relaxing evening and a good night's sleep you're going to be able to think more clearly.' So serious now and gentle. Loretta stood up on unsteady legs and her whole manner invited affection. She thought as she stared up into his face: It could almost be that he knows it is him I love.

He held out an inviting hand; she put hers into it and the next moment she was in his arms, his cool clean breath on her face as his lips came close to possess hers.

'Paul,' she murmured, feeling she had known him a very long time instead of a few short weeks, 'I don't know what I'm up to.' A shuddering sigh escaped her and he took her lips again, this time in a longer, much more passionate kiss.

'Just try to forget everything,' he advised. 'I have said, my dear, that you will feel much better able to think straight after a night's rest.'

She nodded, pressing close as her arms crept up to encircle his neck. My dear. . . . Did it mean anything? He had almost from the first referred to her as 'little one' and that seemed almost like an endearment . . . yet hadn't he mentioned a flirtation? Always she came back to this because always there was Olga, very beautiful and very real, the girl whom everyone believed was soon to marry Paul.

The following morning at breakfast Paul asked her what she intended doing that day, and she was very hesitant about saying that she was going to be with Lee, as it was his day off, and of course she was compelled to add, 'He—he was so happy when I said I loved him that—that he said we'd go to the Club this evening and have a celebration dinner.'

'To celebrate what?' Paul's whole manner changed

and he was regarding her with a steely intentness that plainly revealed his displeasure.

'Well—er—he obviously believes I mean to go to him.' She toyed with her croissant, nervously keeping her head averted.

'Then he's to be disillusioned, isn't he?'

'I can't think any more clearly now than I could last night!' she cried.

'Then allow me to think for you.'

But she shook her head. 'I must spend the day with him.'

'And this evening?'

A deep sigh escaped her. Absently she began buttering the piece of croissant she had broken off. 'I might be able to ask him to leave things as they are for now.'

'Might?' crisply, as he cut himself a piece of bacon.

'I will do,' she said and at that he nodded approvingly.

'What we can do is to all go to the Club tonight,' he then said. 'Olga's fond of dancing and it happens to be Thursday. There'll be a dinner dance on tonight.'

Olga. . . . Well, at least it got her out of having to go alone with Lee, because she rather thought that even though she would tell him she did not wish to celebrate anything he would insist on having the night out with her.

'I'll tell him, then, that you want us to make a foursome.'

Paul said nothing to that and Loretta was left to her own thoughts for a while, which were not happy,

since she knew Lee would not be at all enamoured
by the idea of going out with Paul and Olga when he
had expected to be alone with Loretta. Moreover, he
was going to be puzzled by Paul's invitation, wondering how it had come about in the first place. Loretta
felt faintly resentful of Paul's authoritative behav-
iour yet, paradoxically, she had to admit to being
glad she was not to dine alone with Lee in what
would almost surely have been an intimate situation.

The lights were blazing forth on to the semi-
circular forecourt of the Acacia Club as Paul drew
up to let the girls alight before he drove over to the
parking area. Loretta, dressed in sapphire blue to
match her eyes, had felt well-dressed until she saw
Olga, who wore a model that had surely had its
origin in Paris. Slit right up to the thigh, the skirt was
tight with the kind of cut designed expressly to bring
out a woman's curves. The bodice was tight and so
low-cut that the valley between her breasts was plain
to see. Loretta, on the other hand, wore an Edward-
ian style dress with a prim collar of lace which fitted
snugly at her throat. She wore rather attractive, yet
plain, gold ear drops and a Victorian bracelet which
her aunt had left her along with the money.

Many of the far-flung neighbours were present at
the dinner dance, among them Garth Helmley and
his girl-friend, Edna. At the bar, where little groups
had gathered, drinking aperitifs, Paul introduced
Loretta to several others, two of whom were
bachelors—John Slade and Michael Warmington.
Both seemed unable to disguise their interest in
Loretta and she saw their glances going repeatedly

from her to Lee and back again. Lee was quiet but sociable, far more sociable than she would have expected, for he had been bitterly disappointed when she had told him they couldn't yet have a celebration dinner.

'I must have time to think,' she had added rather lamely and as a result Lee had wanted to know if she had changed her mind.

'No—no, of course not,' she had answered, quite unable to upset him when they were to have a pleasant day together. 'It's only that I haven't had time to think—I did ask you to be patient with me,' she reminded him and he had agreed that this was so.

'Never mind,' he had then said. 'We shall have a nice cosy dinner together anyway.'

A sigh had preceded her words. 'Paul wants us to make a foursome.'

'Paul . . . ?' Lee had glanced strangely at her. 'Why should he want you and me? He's usually been very happy with Olga on his own. Besides, if he wants company then there will be plenty of people there whom he knows.' His bitter disappointment was obvious.

'I suppose it was natural that he should invite us,' returned Loretta with well-assumed casualness. 'I had mentioned that you and I were coming for dinner, you see.'

'Oh.' Nothing more, and if he still thought it strange there was nothing in his manner to show it.

He was now standing close to her, chatting to a man on his right, while Loretta was chatting to Mary and James. There was chatter all around, mingling with music coming from the restaurant, relayed on speakers in the four corners of the room. In the lounge, which spread out from the bar, small tables were scattered about, with rattan chairs and stools to match. A few people were sitting down but more were standing in small groups, glasses in hands, laughing and talking and bringing all the gossip up to date. The women were all attired in long dresses, the men in lounge suits of linen or casual forms of evening dress. Most of the people were farmers of some kind, but some were the tradespeople from the town. Loretta found herself nodding and smiling at the librarian and a few minutes later at the hairdresser from the beauty salon.

'It seems that everyone is here,' laughed Mary, glancing around. 'The dinner dance is always popular but I don't think I've ever seen so many here before. John and Michael scarcely ever come; they're both farming on a small scale and seem to begrudge taking time off for such frivolities as these.'

'How are you liking it here?' from James conversationally when it seemed there might be an awkward pause in the conversation. 'The heat not getting you down?'

'I do find it a little overpowering,' she admitted with a wry grimace, 'especially in the afternoons. However, I'm happy to be here. It's all so new and interesting, and I very much like meeting new people and making friends with them.' She wondered if that sounded a trifle naive, and coloured up on seeing Paul's attention had been caught. He was with Olga and a couple from Salendi Farm who were

114

about their age. Paul caught Loretta's eye and a smile curved his lips. She lowered her lashes, her nerves tingling with nameless sensations. When presently she met his gaze again he was looking at her coolly, deliberately, as if challenging her in some way. Mary suddenly sensed something and turned her head, then slowly turned it again towards Loretta before she glanced with a strange expression at her husband.

There was a sort of electric stillness in the air, noticed by no one except Loretta and Paul and Mary.

Mary said, with a sort of exaggerated casualness, 'How long are you staying, Loretta? Lee's going to miss you when you're gone.'

'I haven't made up my mind.' Loretta glanced up towards where Paul was standing, still looking at her. 'Paul might become fed up with my being around and so I shall have to—er. . . .' She trailed off as Lee turned, his attention caught. 'I really don't know how long I'm staying,' she said, her tone unintentionally curt.

Mary met Lee's eyes. 'You never told us you had such a pretty girl-friend, Lee.'

'We've known one another for several years.'

'But that's interesting,' from a young woman who had been listening without any of the others being aware of it. 'How many years—if it isn't an impertinent question?' The woman laughed lightly and brought a swift frown to Mary's brow.

'It is an impertinent question, Vera, and you know it.' Without pause or a sparing of Vera's feelings Mary turned to Loretta and said, 'Vera's our biggest

115

gossip. She makes a hobby of learning all she can about other people's business.'

'Oh!' The rudeness of Mary's words and manner brought a blush to Loretta's cheeks; she felt she had never been so uncomfortable in her life. Vera had, of course, deserved it, but that did not excuse Mary's forgetting to follow the accepted rules of etiquette.

While she was searching for words Paul came up to her, took her arm and said with quiet authority, 'Let me take you out into the garden, Loretta. I want to show you some rather special shrubs—seeing that you're so interested in the flora of our country.' His grip on her elbow was firm; she tried to hesitate even while welcoming with relief Paul's intervention. She was troubled about Lee, and how he would regard this proprietorial attitude which Paul was exhibiting. His expression was strange but dully resigned. Her heart ached for him, but she was being ushered away and she had no other option than to go with Paul— unless she wanted to bring even more attention to herself by resisting, which she certainly did not.

'I saw the need for rescuing you.' Paul spoke only when they were in the garden, walking away from the glaring lights coming from the many windows and also from the corners of the roof. 'What was happening over there to make you appear so uncomfortable?'

She told him, a quiver in her voice. Her mind was circling around all the tangles that were disrupting her life. 'I'm beginning to feel like going home,' she added in a sort of desperation. 'I could tell Lee that I must go back and think things out. . . .' Her voice trailed because her thoughts had come full circle and she was back to the point where she knew she could not hurt Lee, could not callously leave him, lonely and unhappy and in all probability despairing, believing she had changed her mind and did not love him, as she had so fiercely declared she had in that heartrending moment of impulse when the fact of his crying had proved too much for her tender heart to bear. 'Oh, God, what am I to do!' The cry was an anguished plea for help even though she was well aware no one could help her in the momentous and nerve-pressing decision she must make.

Paul had guided her to a little arbour, silent and dark, well away from the Club buildings. His arms came about her and without hesitation she rested her face against the cool linen of his coat, sensing his anxiety . . . his tenderness.

'Don't upset yourself, little one,' he advised in soft and soothing tones, just as if he were comforting an unhappy child. 'Things have a way of unravelling themselves from the knots we get them into. You're trying to rush and it's unwise. Take your time, and if one day you can't cope then don't try; leave it for another day.'

She lifted her face, shaking her head in a little bewildered mannerism. 'You're so kind to me one moment, Paul, and then you're rough and angry and unfeeling—I wish I could understand you.'

There was a long silence and she nestled closer, savouring the comfort of his breast to lean upon and his strong arms about her.

'You'll probably understand me one day,' he murmured. 'It all depends. . . .'

On what? He had stopped so strangely and she

was recalling with clear distinctness his changes of attitude towards her—mainly since Lee arrived back from his holiday. Paul seemed almost to be balancing on a knife-edge at times, which was absurd, she told herself, but the impression persisted.

'Feeling better now?'

She nodded her head. 'It was Mary's fault in a way,' she said reflectively. 'She was curious—but of course not so forthrightly outspoken as Vera—well, not until the end, when she admonished the woman.'

'Vera's harmless but, as Mary says, the greatest gossip of the lot. She really goes out of her way to probe into the affairs of others no matter how much she is resented. It's a sort of disease, if you ask me,' he added on a note that was suddenly grim.

Loretta said nothing, for her thoughts had switched and she was thinking of Olga, in there at the bar, having seen Paul take another girl out to the garden. Loretta knew that she herself would have been fiercely jealous and upset. Under the impelling force of jealousy Loretta felt she would have been just as vindictive towards Olga as the girl was to her for, after all, she was the one whom everyone expected Paul to marry. Would he marry her in the end? A terrible pain shot through Loretta's head at the idea, then was gone, but she had shivered within the circle of Paul's arms and, bending his head, he kissed her gently on the lips.

'I'm sorry to be like this, Paul. I wish I could think straight, and also that there weren't so many complications in my life.'

'Many?' He was swift to hold her from him, attempting in the darkness to read her expression.

'What else have you on your mind besides this decision you have to make concerning Lee?'

Faintly she smiled. What would he say were she to tell him all that was in her heart and mind? Tell him she loved him with everything she had inside her, and that she sometimes wondered, as now, whether he in turn cared a little for her. Then all at once something indefinable entered the atmosphere, something which seemed to envelop them both, closing them into a net which bound them together. It was a mysterious sensation, unreal and profound; it covered a moment in time that was never to be forgotten by either of them as, ending the supreme tenseness, Paul swept her into his arms and kissed her with the sort of savage tenderness that matched the country in which he had always lived, the primitive country which still boasted of regions untrodden by man.

'You're very lovely,' he whispered close to the tempting hollow of her throat. 'What you must have been like at eighteen I do not know, but all I do know is that, had I been Lee, I'd never ever have let you go.'

She stepped back, lips quivering in unison with her nerves. Paul was intense, vibrantly so, and possessive. What did it mean? If he cared then why didn't he tell her so? But if he did tell her, then where would she be? In a worse situation, surely. Two men loving her—Vehemently she shook her head. It must not be so! Her decision was difficult enough already, but while there was the possibility of Paul's marrying Olga at least her decision lay only with her relationship towards Lee.

'We ought to be going back.' Her voice was urgent suddenly as she realised that dinner must be starting by now. 'We seem to have been here for ages.'

He nodded, and took her hand. They strolled back at a leisurely pace, his hand warm and tight about hers. The night was exciting and mysterious, with the mothy darkness all around them and the crescent moon sailing above amid a billion points of silver twinkling in an African sky of deepest purple. From a great distance there drifted the primordial and haunting throb of a native drum beat, beautiful and sad, like the music made by the scented breeze as it whispered through the leaves of the tall dome palms and the less stately pines. Then the drum was hushed and all was silent but for the whisper of the leaves, but as they drew closer the tantalising cadence of an alabaster fountain was the prelude to entry into the Club grounds proper where lights flared and music of a very different kind could be heard coming from the restaurant where, on a large glass circle, several couples were dancing. Paul stopped, drew Loretta close and, bending his dark head, he kissed her gently on the lips.

Chapter Seven

Loretta watched broodingly as Paul danced with Olga, and at the same time she was profoundly conscious of Lee's watching her—as if he were curious about her interest in Paul and Olga. She turned and smiled and began to chat, noticing, however, that Lee gave very little attention to the conversation. It was an interval between courses and the floor was fairly crowded, so Lee hadn't asked her to dance, knowing how she hated being bumped against people. Besides, it was very warm and on the actual floor the heat would have been suffocating.

'It's not the dinner we'd planned, is it Loretta?' She heard the question after her eyes had been drawn even yet again to the impressive couple on the floor, a couple who danced together superbly, whose bodies were close, whose poise matched as did their superlative looks. Nature and a long line of ancestry had in each case produced something very special. They were well-matched, in looks, height, poise, and even in dress. Loretta felt shabby in comparison to Olga.

'Not exactly,' she agreed after a pause, then added, with a lightness that was forced, 'But we're enjoying it all the same, aren't we, Lee?'

His eyes were curiously intent as they rested on her lovely face. 'Are you enjoying it to the full?' he asked with an odd inflection.

'Of course,' a little too swiftly, she realised on noting his expression. 'Aren't you?'

He was more frank than she. 'No, Loretta, I am not enjoying it to the full.'

She sighed and glanced away; she felt his warm hand cover hers. 'You lied when you said you love me, didn't you?'

The words startled her and yet, somehow, they did not altogether surprise her. 'Lee . . . I—'

'You have no need to apologise, dear,' he broke in gently. 'It was only to be expected that you would fall in love with Paul.'

Silence; she had nothing to say to that. In any case, her mouth felt too dry for her to articulate words, and so it was Lee who eventually spoke, a twisted smile on his face.

'It's generally believed that he and Olga will marry.'

'Yes, I know,' with a quiver in her voice.

'She has everything a man like he could want.'

Loretta nodded dumbly.

'Wealth,' said Lee slowly, as if to allow each word to sink in. 'Beauty, elegance, ancestry, poise.'

Loretta looked at the girl under discussion. 'All those,' she murmured, 'while I have none of them.'

'You have beauty, dear. To me, Loretta, you surpass them all—everyone here tonight. You always will be the loveliest girl I have ever known.'

Her mouth trembled convulsively. She stared at him through anguished eyes. 'What are we to do, Lee?' she quavered. 'What is to be the end of it all?' If only she hadn't come! But fate, capricious fate, had brought her here and the plight she was in was crucifying her.

Lee withdrew his hand. 'I could make you love me, darling.' His voice was low and pleading, the cry of anguish equal to her own. 'I know I can make you happy. I'd cherish you and care for you—Loretta, if you throw in your lot with me, my beloved, you'll never regret it. I swear to you that never in my life will I do anything to hurt you—no, not even to upset you.'

She turned away, pressing a hand to her heart. Paul was looking at her; she saw a dark frown spread over his brow.

He looked so stern and forbidding. If the impossible could be attained and she could be married to him, *he* would hurt her at times—not physically, of course, but his displeasure, however slight, would never fail to inflict abominable pain. She turned to Lee again, examining his dear, familiar face. No, he would never hurt her. He would nurture her, shield her from all pain, from the cold winds of reality, even. It would be a quiet, companionable relationship, with each being kind to the other, caring, respecting . . . but on her side not loving. She knew she could never love anyone but Paul, feared that, married to Lee, she would perhaps pretend that it was Paul making love to her. . . . A great shudder of self-disgust passed through her; it was visible and occurred at the very moment that Paul and Olga returned to the table.

He looked down into Loretta's eyes with a steely intentness, his face hard, his mouth compressed. 'Something the matter?' he inquired bluntly, eyes flitting to Lee.

'No, of course not.'

The two sat down, Olga with all that was scrupulously correct—the glance first at the chair, the gentle feel for its edge with the back of her leg, the tilting of her skirt with a forward swing, and then the actual sitting down and relaxing, head held high, arrogance in every single inch of her.

'You don't look too happy.'

'Paul, darling, it isn't nice to make remarks like that,' smoothly from Olga with a sort of exaggerated charm. 'Loretta and Lee might have been having a lovers' tiff.'

A small silence followed, with Lee's mouth compressing. It was very plain that he did not like Olga, and equally plain that she did not like him, since the half-contemptuous glance she cast at him was proof enough of her opinion of him.

'I assure you we have not had a tiff,' said Lee presently. 'Loretta and I get along far too well for unnecessary things like quarrelling. Disharmony is something we both abhor.' Cool the tone and controlled, dignified, too, and Paul's interest was caught. Loretta gained the impression that Paul was seeing something in Lee he had never seen before.

'How very comfortable for you.' Olga's voice was bitten with acid and all three glanced at her. 'You must be unique,' she added, as if she had to. And then, as though realising she might have gone too far, she affected impatience as she said to Paul, 'How long is the next course going to be, I wonder?'

'There's no hurry. We're here for the evening.' His glance went to Loretta. 'Care to dance?' he said.

She rose slowly, reluctantly, because she knew Lee would not care for her to be dancing with Paul, whom he now knew she loved. She caught Olga's glittering gaze, and Lee's brooding one, before she was swung away with an imperious gesture and she found herself in Paul's arms, brought close to his hard body . . . too close, unnecessarily so.

'You're not all joy,' was his crisp opening once they were away from the table. '*Was* it a lovers' tiff, as Olga suggested?' The voice was hardening with every word spoken, and when she glanced up it was to see an implacable face set in unapproachable lines.

'Lee spoke the truth,' was her taut rejoinder. 'Olga needs a lesson in manners!'

'And so do I, you're saying.' Paul's voice was grim.

'Lee and I were having a serious discussion which concerned no one but ourselves.' She continued to look up at him, wondering what he would say if he were to know the real gist of the conversation.

'He was asking you to throw in your lot with him?'

'Lee would never try to persuade me. . . .' She trailed off to silence, recalling his earnest assertion that he could make her happy, that in actual fact he had begged her to throw in her lot with him.

Paul stiffened against her and said perceptively, 'So he did try to persuade you?'

'He said he could make me happy. I know he could.'

'Even though you don't love him?'

'People have married without love.' She thought of Olga, whom she could have said without any doubt at all was not in love with Paul. And what of Paul's feelings for her? Nothing of the ardent lover about him!

'But not people like you,' grimly, as he brought her to him in order to avoid collision with another couple, the action rough and angry, and she had the impression that nothing would have given him greater satisfaction than to shake her thoroughly.

'I feel so sorry for Lee—'

'But you promised you would not allow pity to influence you.'

'You forced the promise from me!'

'And I mean you to keep it—even if I have to speak with Lee myself,' was his grim and decisive threat. She leant away, scanning his face. So formidable! With that implacable set of the jaw and the uncompromising line of his mouth. Heaven help any who crossed him—really crossed him!

'Please don't interfere, Paul,' she found herself pleading. 'Lee and I must sort this out for ourselves.'

He was shaking his head. He had guided her towards the verandah and as it dawned on her that his intention was to take her outside she voiced a swift and firm protest. 'The meal will be on the table—we can't—'

'The course won't be served until we get to the table.' Already he had her outside and was steering her towards the darkness from which they had emerged less than an hour ago.

But for the moment the lights from the Club windows were still on them and she looked up into his face, a face with harsh forbidding contours, eyes like flint and an inflexible, out-thrust jaw. His figure seemed just as forbidding, sparse and upright, lithe as a tiger's. She drew back but he urged her on; she asked what his intention was but recevied no answer.

'I want this thing cleared up,' he snapped, speaking at last when they were well away from the lights. 'You're dithering! I won't allow you to change your mind—get that!'

'Who do you think you are?' she demanded, having taken more from him than she could stand. This interference was as puzzling as it was irritating. 'I've enough on my mind without you taking me over like this! You forget your place—we're host and guest but you've assumed authority over me almost from the first! Who do you think you are?' she demanded again, unwanted tears filling her eyes. She hated dissention between Paul and herself.

'You can't think logically and practically, and so it is my duty to think for you! I intend to speak to Lee, and this very evening! That is what I have brought you out here to tell you—' An imperative flick of the finger stopped the interruption he guessed she intended to make. 'Had I told you in there, while we were dancing, you'd have protested and people would have noticed, so that's why you're here now. Lee must be told that you don't love him and, therefore, you can't marry him when he gets the divorce he's contemplating!'

'Lee knows I don't love him,' she informed him quietly. 'He guessed it for himself.' She knew she was pale and that she was as tense as it was possible to be, with every nerve-end and cell in her body touched by the riot of emotional stress that was affecting her both physically and mentally. She felt oblivion would be welcome, for at least she would be out of her misery.

'He guessed?' in a faintly startled tone. 'When did he guess? You'd told him you loved him; he'd not have expected you to lie.'

'He guessed tonight—'

'Tonight?' with sharp and swift interrogation. He was standing close; she could smell the heady male odour of him, musky, tempting. . . . 'When?'

'When you were dancing with Olga—' She stopped abruptly, aware that he must surely be puzzled by an answer like that. With his mood as it was he'd be sure to demand a fuller explanation.

'I see. . . .' With a quality of perception in his voice. 'He guessed then, did he? I wonder why?'

She shook her head in the darkness, the colour coming back into her cheeks. 'I don't know.'

'I rather think you do, little one.'

'Please don't harass me like this,' she begged. 'And I want to go back—at once, if you don't mind.'

'I meant what I said about having this out with

Lee. Even though he's guessed you don't love him he wants you to go to him. Can't you accept that he's adopting a most selfish attitude?'

'You don't understand,' she cried, 'because you don't know everything! Oh, for God's sake, take me back in there!'

'Not while you're in this wrought-up state.' He took her to him, jerking her when she would have resisted. 'Loretta, the time has come when I can tell you what you ought to have guessed already.' So quiet and grave the tone, so gentle the hand stroking her hair.

She leant away as he would have taken her lips, and said with a quivering sigh that was almost a sob, 'What—what should I h-have guessed, Paul—oh, tell me!' Yet she dreaded the words she knew were to come, for this was the situation she had known would only serve to disturb her mind even more than it was disturbed already.

'I love you, Loretta, and intend to marry you. I don't think I'm mistaken in surmising that the reason why Lee made that guess tonight was because of your expression when you were watching Olga and me dancing. I'm right, aren't I?'

She nodded her head, her heart full even while it dragged within her. It sang while it cried; one part of her was on air and the other was sinking into the depths of despair. What was to be the end of it all, now that Paul had confessed his love?

'Yes,' she admitted, burying her face in his coat and hoping her lip rouge would not leave a stain. 'He guessed because of my expression.'

'Of course, *I* had almost guessed—in fact, recently, I was sure you cared for me, but Lee stood between us. I felt you would sacrifice yourself rather than hurt him and so I demanded that promise from you. Oh, yes, I knew you regarded me as an ogre, a dictatorial, interfering man who had no right to dig his oar in—but I did have a right, Loretta, the right of the man who intends to become your husband.' Firm the declaration and possessive the kiss that followed. Loretta gave herself up to his love-making, thrilling to his gentle caresses and murmurings and for this one blissful interlude she was able to forget Lee, and her troubles, forget everything but the fact that Paul loved her, that he had not been flirting after all, but had been in deadly earnest, determined to make her his wife.

His wife. . . . If only there were no stumbling block, no clouds on the horizon. If only Lee weren't so nice, so kind and lovable, so sincere in his desire to make her happy.

'Paul,' she said after his ardour had cooled a little and he was holding her from him, endeavouring to see her face in the gloom, 'say you won't speak to Lee tonight—or any other time. Promise me. I want to sort it out on my own—'

'There isn't any sorting out to do,' he broke in implacably. 'You and I shall announce our engagement—'

'No! I can't be so cruel! I must have time to think of some way of easing the pain Lee will feel. Besides, there's Olga as well,' she added as the thought occurred to her.

'I shall deal with Olga.'

'But everyone believes you're almost engaged—you know they do.'

The suggestion of an amused smile lifted the corners of his mouth. 'What are you trying to do, make me feel a cad?'

'She's going to be dreadfully upset.' Loretta had almost said 'hurt,' but doubted if the girl was the kind to feel hurt. Rather would she be furious, and perhaps vindictive, should the opportunity arise.

'Just as Lee will,' Paul returned calmly. 'But, as I once said, my little one, we each have one life to live and we can't afford to waste any of it, not a single day. You and I love one another so where is the sense of our marrying someone else?'

'I haven't told you I love you. . . .' She was shy and blushing, her head coming down to find a resting place against his shoulder, and her arm slid around his neck. 'I love you, dearest Paul—love you to distraction.'

'Which is just how it should be,' he said with a kind of bland assurance. She gave a little protesting cry and called him arrogant and self-opinionated. Her reward was a playful shaking before her mouth was crushed beneath the moist and ardent pressure of his. For a long moment she thrilled to his passionate caresses, his hard possessive body compelling hers to obey the demand of the rhythmic movement of his own lithe and muscular frame. His hand stole gently into her dress after he had deftly dealt with the tiny pearl buttons and she quivered ecstatically as the warmth closed around her breast—a hand gentle and loving, caressing and teasing until the little bud was stiff and upright, its desire relaying

131

waves of ecstasy into her loins so that she arched and pushed, aided by the pressure of Paul's other hand. She wanted nothing more than to stay out here all night, forgetting those inside who were waiting . . . and wondering. This was magic, this night of revelation, this blue night of stars and an ice pale moon, an African night with a drumbeat in the distance and the trilling of cicadas close by, thousands of them, in the trees. Suddenly, though, reality hit her and she heard herself say, her mouth tender and sacrificial against his ear, 'The dinner, Paul,' and then she felt exceedingly foolish because he laughed, then tugged her hair and finally chided her for being unromantic.

'Nevertheless,' he conceded as he tidied her hair by stroking it with cupped hands which glided gently down to lift her face, 'I must agree. We have to go in, sweet, and take part in mundane chatter while our minds are occupied with things far, far different.'

She nodded and fell into step beside him. All was silent and still; the mountains were black shapes against the sky, with matching remoteness, but there was a haunting beauty about them, an impression of eternal peace. The bushveld lay slumbering, its vastness drugged by the lullaby of the wind soughing in the palms and low bushes—acacias and prickly pears. Everything was caressed by starlight, pure and timeless as on the day it was created. With a sigh between pleasure and pain Loretta sought for the comfort of her lover's body; he stopped to assuage her desperate need, holding her tenderly against him, stroking her hair and her face, caressing her throat with his lips.

'I'm so confused. . . .' She hadn't meant to say

anything like that but it came out, spilled out, from a heart torn between pity for one man and love for another.

And through it all came the conviction—which she could not shake off—that Lee's claim on her was stronger than Paul's. . . .

Chapter Eight

To Loretta's relief Paul agreed not to speak to Lee just yet awhile.

'But don't forget,' he went on warningly, pointing an imperious finger at her, 'I want our engagement to be announced without much delay. I'm not a patient man, my love. I want you soon!'

'You have to speak to Olga,' she returned desperately.

'I shall do that without delay.'

Loretta sighed and watched with relief as he went off, along the mosquito-netted corridor towards the apartment at the end which was his study. She had the morning free, and it was again her intention to go over to Lee's house, although she felt sure he would not be there. However, to her surprise he *was* there, not having gone to work because he was feeling ill. He looked it, too, as he lay back against the cushions on the rattan couch. His face was grey and seemed to have sunken in. Frightened, Loretta moved swiftly, to kneel beside him and lay a soothing hand upon his head.

'What's wrong?' she asked rather fearfully. 'You're so hot, Lee.'

'I don't know, unless it's the fever. I was a little groggy last night when I got back, but thought I'd be all right after a night's sleep.'

'You didn't sleep, though?'

He shook his head. 'No, darling, I didn't—but it wasn't altogether due to the way I felt physically.' A thin smile touched the dry, parched outline of his mouth.

'You were worrying about us?' The words were difficult to say and even more difficult was the reassuring smile she gave to him. 'Don't worry about that, dear Lee. Just for the present, we must concentrate on getting you well.' She paused a moment, instinctively knowing that it was the fever that had brought him down. Paul had told her about it, and how it came suddenly and laid you low for days before eventually leaving you drained and listless and feeling you would never be right again.

'You have had it?' she had asked Paul.

'I have,' with a grim inflection. 'And I'd not wish it on my worst enemy. However, it does happen to be one of the hazards.' Paul had looked at her and added that he hoped she would never be laid low with it.

And now here was Lee, living alone. . . .

'Can I get you anything?' she asked, even while she was wondering if she ought to run back and get Paul at once. To give Lee something, even a drink, might do more harm than good at this stage of the illness.

'A drink of water, that's all.'

She fetched it, watched him drink thirstily, then took the glass from him again. 'You shouldn't have come from your bed, Lee. I'm off to bring Paul, who'll get you back there and then send for the doctor.'

Lee nodded lethargically, moving by determined will-power to get himself more comfortable on the couch. His whole body seemed leaden, and he winced as if he had excruciating pains in his head.

'God,' he moaned, 'the heat's searing through me in waves—' But he broke off, shivering as if he had the ague.

'I must go and fetch Paul,' she said urgently and hastened away, reluctant to leave him and yet more reluctant to waste any more time.

Paul's face was a study when she told him about Lee. 'It certainly sounds very much like the fever,' he said grimly. 'I'll phone the hospital and ask them to be prepared to accept him.'

'But it might not be the fever—'

'Then there's no harm done.'

It was the fever, declared Paul after casting an eye over Lee's face. It was soaked in perspiration and his eyes looked as if they were burned right into their sockets.

Paul helped Lee to his feet and Loretta supported

his other side. Paul had brought his car right up to the door so there was no delay in getting Lee to the hospital in Falburg.

'He looks bad.' The doctor frowned and shook his head. Fearfully Loretta said, as Lee was taken away and they were left alone in the cold, tile-lined passage, 'People don't die of the fever, do they?'

He studied her intently for a space before answering her question. 'Lee won't die,' he assured her, his gaze still intent. 'But he's going to be weak for some time to come.'

'I shall look after him.'

A frown touched Paul's dark brow. 'We can get a nurse.'

'I daresay, but I feel it is my duty to care for him.' She was pale, fighting hard to get her own way, determined to get it, but unbearably depressed because she knew she was angering Paul. 'I couldn't leave him to a nurse. It would be callous.'

'And so you intend to go to his house every day?'

She nodded, mouth quivering. 'Don't be angry, Paul,' she beseeched. 'Try to understand just how I feel.'

His face remained hard, like granite. 'And what would Lee have done if you hadn't come here in the first place?'

'The question's superfluous. I did come. I'm here and I can help him during his recovery.' Her pallor was more pronounced than ever as she said, 'You forget, Paul, that if I hadn't come here in the first place then you and I would never have met, and you wouldn't now be in a position to dictate to me.'

His mouth went tight; she felt that nothing would afford him greater satisfaction than to shake her.

'Let us get out of here,' he said harshly. 'I'll phone later to see when he can have visitors—' He stopped as the doctor in his white coat came through a door on their right.

'Best leave the visiting for at least a full day,' he advised. 'It's a severe case. He'll not know you anyway.'

Paul nodded his head. 'I'll give you a ring,' he said and a moment later he and Loretta were outside in the sunshine, away from antiseptic smells and the cold austerity of the hospital environment.

'I feel terrible.' Loretta stood by the car while Paul unlocked the door. He was close and she could smell his after-shave. He glanced down into her face and she saw that his was grim. 'It's—unfortunate,' she murmured without realising he might take it the wrong way.

'In that our engagement must be postponed?'

'I meant—oh, Paul, I don't know what I meant!' He said nothing; his mouth was grim and she just stood there, looking up at him in wordless misery until, impatiently, he ushered her into the car. He drove into the grounds of the Club and she asked no questions, for her mind and body seemed numb. Last night she had lain awake for a long while, trying to sort out her life. She had made a determined resolution which was to tell Lee that Paul loved her and, therefore, she must marry him. Lee, she felt, had more claim on her than Paul, but on the other hand she came to the decision that she could not hurt Paul. There was also the vital circumstance of her own feelings; she knew she would make a better wife to a man she loved than to one for whom she felt only compassion, no matter how deep and sincere that compassion was.

But now. . . . How could she tell Lee that she was finished with him? He was ill, and would not be himself again for a long time. Paul, meanwhile, would become impatient—was already impatient with her for insisting on caring for Lee herself instead of letting him hire a nurse.

'I know you're angry with me,' she faltered, breaking the tense silence at last. 'But if only you would try to understand my position it would help. Lee and I were in love—oh, I know it was a long time ago! But there was something deep, which I can't just forget and throw aside as you want me to. I must take care of him, Paul; I must!' At the plea in her voice his face softened. He had stopped the car and now he turned to her, slipping an arm across the back of her seat.

'And after you have nursed him back to health?'

'I can think more clearly.'

'Well,' he conceded, surprising her, 'you can do what you consider your duty. But as soon as Lee is perfectly well again you shall tell him about us.'

'Well . . .'

'Or I shall,' was his firm assertion as he slid from the driver's seat and came swiftly round to open her door for her. 'When the time comes you can make your choice.'

She got out and they went into the restaurant

where coffee and biscuits were being served. Paul ordered a pot of coffee and some toasted teacakes, which at first Loretta refused.

'Eat something,' Paul ordered imperiously. 'Your stomach's churning over.'

'How do you know?'

'I happen to know *you*. You're a bag of nerves; you'll be ill yourself if you are not very careful.' He sounded hard, she thought, but there was the trace of a tender smile on his face when she looked at him across the table.

She picked up a hot buttered teacake and took a bite. It was delicious and she was soon taking another, aware of Paul's approving gaze.

'Good girl,' he said when she had finished.

She smiled wanly, comparing him to Lee. Both were good looking, but of course Lee seemed so very much older than Paul. It was sad what the years did to you, she thought, aware that Paul would be as old as Lee one day—but she would be older, too, not too far behind Paul . . . if she married Paul, that was.

'Penny for them?' he said softly and her smile became brighter now.

'It wasn't important, Paul. As a matter of fact, I was thinking of growing old—and what the years do to you.'

'Growing old is something none of us can avoid. Its only compensation is that everyone else is growing old with you.'

She nodded automatically. 'Lee looked very old today.'

'Illness is bad for the looks.'

'He'll soon be forty-eight.'

'Not old, Loretta, just too old for you, that's all.' He looked intently at her. 'You've realised this at last?'

'At present it isn't important—well, not too important. But as you once mentioned, it's in another ten or twenty years that we should realise the importance of the age gap.'

'Well, I wouldn't trouble that lovely head of yours with it. You'll not be marrying Lee; you'll be marrying me. I'm five years older . . . just enough to be able to show you who's the boss,' he added in some amusement, just as if he had to.

Her smile quivered. 'Lee cares so deeply about me, Paul,' she began, knowing he'd be impatient with her yet unable to refrain from saying what was in her mind. 'How am I going to tell him I can't marry him?'

'He doesn't know yet that I love you—? No, he can't, since you'd not have told him this morning, and you only knew yourself last night—although you ought to have guessed,' he added with a sudden shake of his head. 'I was always led to believe that a woman's intuition was something rather wonderful.'

'I did wonder if you cared,' she answered reminiscently. 'But then it seemed that you were only flirting with me—in fact, you did mention the word flirtation. Also, there was Olga, who seemed far more fitted to be your wife than—' She was stopped abruptly by the lifting of his finger.

His eyes were dark and stern as he said, 'You, Loretta, are the only woman fitted to be my wife. I love you, and I have never loved Olga.'

'There was a time, though, when you thought you might marry her.'

'I agree—before you came along, or shall we say until just after you came along? I very soon became attracted to you,' he went on frankly, 'and that was why I didn't want you to leave here. I wanted to get to know you, and when I did know you I loved you.'

She looked curiously at him. 'But you knew all along that it was Lee I'd come to see.'

'I also knew Lee was married.'

'But willing to get a divorce.' She paused, expecting him to comment, but he remained silent and after a space she added, 'What is she like—Lee's wife?'

'A charming woman—small and dainty and looking much younger than her years.'

'You sound as if you liked her.' Loretta recalled that she had had the same impression once before when Paul had mentioned Flora to her.

'I did like her, a lot,' he responded thoughtfully. 'I never did understand just what happened. They always seemed so happy together—'

'They did? Happy?' interrupted Loretta in some surprise. Lee had said very little about his wife, now she came to think about it. . . . She had taken for granted that he and she had been unhappy together for some time before the separation.

'Yes, Loretta,' answered Paul with emphasis and looking straight at her. 'Happy. What went wrong no one knows except the couple themselves, but everyone here was amazed when the marriage broke up.'

Loretta was frowning heavily, feeling she ought to have asked Lee more about his wife. 'She just walked out?' she inquired after a pause.

'I believe so. Lee merely told people that he and Flora had decided to go their separate ways.'

'You said, when I first came here, that Lee had gone to Durban hoping to effect a reconciliation?' She was excceedingly puzzled, and not a little disturbed at her omission in finding out more concerning the separation between Lee and his wife who, it would seem, was a likeable sort of woman.

'Most of us concluded that was his reason for going to Durban. It was mere conjecture, though,' he added reflectively. 'Lee has been uncommunicative about the affair right from the start.'

Loretta fell silent, brooding on what Paul had just been saying to her. Surely, she thought, the couple hadn't parted owing to nothing more than a tiff! Yet it did seem, from what she had learned, that Lee and his wife had not been too unhappy in their life together. Moreover, when she came to consider what she knew of Lee's character, she could not for one moment imagine his marrying unless his love for the woman was strong.

'It's a puzzle. . . .' She spoke her thoughts aloud, looking at Paul with that frown still marring her wide, intelligent forehead. 'I'd very much like to meet Lee's wife.'

'There isn't much chance of your doing so,' he returned but he, too, was frowning now. 'If they managed to get together again then it would solve your problem. Is that what you are thinking?'

'I wasn't thinking about myself,' she denied. 'I was concerned entirely with Lee and his future. From what you say it would seem to me that the quarrel which parted them was—well, if not exactly trivial, then not as serious as one would have expected.' Her concern was shadowed in her eyes, and a sudden tenderness erased any last vestige of hardness which had remained in Paul's eyes.

'You're rather sweet,' he told her unexpectedly, 'and rather special too.' With tenderness he laid a hand over hers; the action brought a lightness to her heart but, paradoxically, a tear to her eye.

She brushed it away, saying with a forced little laugh, 'I'm rather silly, too—crying just because you are kind to me.'

'I'm not always kind, little one,' he said after a small pause. 'But remember, darling, that if I appear to be hard and unfeeling it's because I mean it for your own good. You made me a promise not to allow pity to influence your decision regarding Lee, and I shall see that you keep that promise.' He withdrew his hand but kept his eyes upon her, subjecting her to a very searching scrutiny. 'I'm not a fool, Loretta,' he went on presently. 'I can see indecision in your eyes the whole time. I feel sure that you'd sacrifice yourself for Lee, but remember that you would be sacrificing me, too, and *that* I shall not accept. You're mine,' he continued vibrantly and with the old familiar arrogance and mastery, 'and see that you never forget it. Understand?'

She moistened her lips. 'Yes,' she murmured at last. 'Yes, Paul, I understand.'

The tawny eyes were glinting. 'You're still undecided,' he said almost harshly, and it was only then that Loretta realised that in spite of his dictatorial manner, his apparent confidence in his own ability to force her to his will, he was in fact troubled, aware that in the end she would make her own decision—yes, coerce her he might, but the final decision would be hers alone.

She went with Paul to see Lee. He was in a bad way, with no interest in either of them. Swathed in blankets, he was perspiring continuously, but even as they watched he began to shiver—great shuddering spasms passing through him. Few words were spoken, because Lee had no inclination to answer, and so they came away after only a few minutes.

Once outside, the doctor came and assured them that there would be an improvement in a couple of days' time. 'His temperature'll be down and he'll be feeling much better.'

Paul nodded, spoke kindly to the black nurse who had been in the ward as they entered but was at this moment walking along the passage, and then, taking Loretta's arm, he ushered her from the clinical atmosphere of the hospital into the bright and brittle sunshine of an African afternoon.

'Don't look so troubled,' he said. 'You heard what the doctor said.'

'I know—but, Paul, he's so uncomfortable, with that blanket wrapped all around him. Why can't they just tuck it in, as one usually does. I should hate that rough thing clinging to me like that.'

'It's a necessity during the first few days.'

'He was unfortunate to contract the disease like that.'

Paul said nothing; he was thoughtful and fell into a somewhat brooding silence. Loretta wished she could know what his thoughts were at this moment.

They got into the car and drove back to Rikuyu Lodge in silence. Loretta was troubled by Paul's manner as he seemed remote somehow, and introspective . . . a long way from her. And on their arrival at the homestead he offered only a brief word of excuse and went off to his study.

It was mid-afternoon and she decided to take the runabout and have an hour or so in town. She would go to the library, she decided, and then have tea at the Club. The sun was hot and she wore a big flowered hat in stiff linen, for her hair at the front was becoming rather more bleached than she wished it to be. After leaving the library, where she had chosen a couple of novels she had been wanting to read for some time, she drove along the dusty main street and turned in at the Club entrance. And the first person she saw was Garth Helmley, parking his car. He slipped from the driver's seat, and came up to her, a smile on his rugged brown face. Of medium height, and carrying a little more flesh than was necessary, he was yet attractive—with a mass of blond hair and light blue eyes, a spontaneous smile which was reflected in his gaze now as he looked at Loretta with interest not unmingled with curiosity.

'Hello, Loretta! All alone?'

'Yes,' she answered, automatically falling into step

with him as he made his way towards the Club entrance. 'I felt at loose ends so came into town.' She paused a second. 'Did you know that Lee has a fever?'

Garth's eyes widened. 'I didn't know. Is he very bad?'

Loretta nodded and gave a small sigh. 'Yes, as a matter of fact, he is.'

'He'll be weak for some time. How long has he been in hospital?'

'He went in yesterday morning. Paul and I have just been along to see him. He looks awful.' Distress caused her voice to catch; Garth sent her a sideways glance and fell oddly silent until they were seated together at a small table in one corner of the restaurant. He and she had taken it for granted that they'd share a table and a pot of tea.

'You knew Lee some years ago.' A statement and she merely inclined her head in an affirmative gesture. 'The separation was a mystery to everyone.' Abrupt the tone but very quiet.

Loretta had the impression that although he felt he should not pursue the subject he was being forced by some impulse he could not control. She said guardedly, deliberately encouraging him, 'You knew Flora well?'

'Very well. She's a lovely girl—and by that I don't mean only in looks; Flora has a beautiful personality.' He paused, looking across at her, but she made no comment and he went on, 'Lee's a charming bloke, too, and they seemed so well matched—and happy.'

Loretta, tensed and feeling a sudden chill throughout her body, asked slowly, 'Has no one any idea what caused the break?'

Garth shook his head, frowning reflectively. 'I used to visit them occasionally and was always struck by the happiness that used to come through from them both.'

Loretta's mouth felt dry.. 'Then whatever happened to part them? It's so sad, Garth, and it troubles me greatly.'

His eyes met hers and he hesitated before answering. 'I wouldn't know for sure, because Flora just walked out on him, and Lee has been close about it, but I have an idea that Lee had someone else—'

'Someone else? Lee?' Loretta shook her head angrily. 'He'd never be unfaithful to any woman. I can vouch for that!' It was perhaps natural that her vehemence should bring an expression of surprise to her companion's eyes. But before he had time to say anything Loretta was speaking again. 'How did you come to reach a conclusion like that?' she asked.

'Something Lee let out inadvertently—something I don't think he even knew he was saying.'

'Yes?'

'I was there one evening—felt I had to drop in because he'd been so lonely and lost after she went. Lee was obviously not intending to talk about Flora, but because I was so curious I managed subtly to mention her and it was after we'd talked for only a few minutes—during which time I'd learned precious little as to the reason for the break—that he said, almost to himself, "She saw the photograph and asked me about her—" Lee stopped there and his face closed. I knew I'd get nothing more from him.'

'She saw a photograph. . . .' Fate again! Anger and frustration mingled to bring colour to Loretta's cheeks. The photograph would be hers, the only one Lee had, the one he insisted on Loretta having taken just before he left so that he could take it with him to Africa. And he had kept it. . . . Foolish, *foolish* Lee! But why hadn't he been able to explain?

'So it would seem, from what Lee said. You know, it's a funny thing but I, like you, can't imagine Lee's ever being unfaithful to his wife.'

'He definitely wasn't unfaithful,' asserted Loretta, half inclined to tell him the truth. However, she refrained, aware as she was how quickly gossip spread around here; she had no wish to fill people's mouths with something that could be twisted and turned and added to as it passed from one tongue to another.

'You seem very sure,' curiously and with a faintly perplexed expression. 'You knew him well in the old days, it would seem?'

'Very well,' she answered non-committally and thereon changed the subject, talking of the coming Yacht Club Dance and the polo match next Saturday in which both Garth and Paul would be taking part. Garth, though plainly still curious and wanting to learn more about the relationship once existing between Loretta and Lee, respected her wish to let the subject drop.

'Have you ever watched a polo match?' he asked and, when Loretta shook her head, 'You'll find it fast and exciting. This coming match is the highlight of the season, as the cup is being presented—we've been playing a knock-out competition, as you will probably know?'

'Yes, both Lee and Paul explained a little about it to me.'

'We've been having practice *chukkas* but we've our work cut out to beat the other team.'

'Is Paul a good player?'

'Very good. He's an experienced campaigner and highly proficient.'

'And you?' She laughed as she spoke and added quickly, 'I ought not to ask a question like that, ought I?'

He caught her laughter. 'I don't mind admitting I'm not one of the best. But I enjoy the game and always hope to improve. I haven't been playing long,' he added finally.

'I'm looking forward to seeing the match, since it will be a new experience.' Her mind was very far from such things as polo tournaments, though; it was occupied mainly with the information she had received just now from Garth, and she felt that there had been a deep love between Lee and his wife. She recalled Paul's opinion of the affair—the way he, too, had been sure that the couple were happy together. What, then, had happened? Lee could surely have explained about the photograph? Loretta's mind was circling, like a vortex out of control, for she was now looking at the fact that Lee had seemed to be so genuinely in love with *her*, his old flame. He wanted to divorce Flora. A man could not be in love with two women at one and the same time, and on the face of it it did seem that it was Loretta whom he loved.

'You look troubled.' Garth's quiet voice recalled her and she looked up with a smile and a rather rueful shake of her head.

'It was nothing,' she said, fully aware she was not deceiving him. 'Have you finished, Garth?'

'Yes—I'm ready to leave when you are.'

They strolled to the car park together, through exotic gardens and a colourful shrubbery on the way.

Once back at the homestead she went to her room and then out on to the *stoep*, her brow creased in a thoughtful frown. Undoubtedly something should be done to help Lee and Flora get together again—and she was not thinking of herself in the least. She was thinking entirely of Lee, remembering his unhappiness, his heartbreaking loneliness. She was restless, feeling frustrated at her inability to act . . . and yet what action could she take even when Lee was up and about again? He would not tolerate interference even from her.

With an impatient movement she went into her bedroom and through it to the bathroom. A shower refreshed her body but not her mind; she felt almost listless as she dressed in a long flowered skirt with a simple, short-sleeved white silk blouse to go with it. It was still early so she went out to the garden, revelling in the cool of early evening after the gruelling heat of the sun earlier, especially at midday and for the couple of hours following. The sprinklers were working on the main lawn, and Marylou, wife of the head gardener, was busy watering the borders. It was not work which she had to do, but as she had once told Loretta, she enjoyed being in the garden if she had a few hours, or even moments, to spare.

'It's cool now, miss.' She smiled as Loretta came up to her. 'The flowers are thirsty so I water them.'

'I expect they are thanking you.' Loretta smiled in return and strolled on, past beds of roses, of verbenas and canna lilies and passion flowers. Two bright butterflies moved daintily, hovering on transparent wings, and from the trees could be heard the winging of beetles and the inevitable whirring of cicadas. The sun was sinking and the mountains were looming dark against the sky. A line of low palms waved gently, their backcloth the *kopjes* which, as always, were at this time of day taking on mysterious shapes, like something weird and wonderful from a fantasy film. The bushveld, which had been shimmering in the pitiless and suffocating heat of the sun, was already drowsy and cool and silent in its primordial solitude. Loretta's body swung around to face the citrus groves in the other direction, groves which seemed to stretch for endless miles, the healthy trees in long straight lines with watercourses—man made —between them.

Her mind switched off from all around her as once again she began thinking of Lee and Flora. But it was Lee especially who was her main anxiety at this time, for she wondered what toll the fever would take of his resources. He had seemed so very weak . . . almost as if he were ready to give up hope. . . .

'So there you are, my dear.' Paul's voice brought

152

her body round and a swift smile to her lips.
'Enjoying the cool of the evening, eh?' His appreciative glance swept over her in swift appraisal before
his eyes returned to her face. 'You look charming—
as always.'

'Thank you,' demurely and with a hint of rising
colour.

Paul fell into step beside her as they made their
way back to the house. She waited until they were
inside before broaching the subject which was giving
her so much trouble. She told him what Garth had
said and saw him nod his head thoughtfully.

'Isn't there something we can do?' she asked
finally, her big eyes anxious and appealing as she
lifted her face to his.

A moment of silence followed before Paul said,
ignoring her question for the time being, 'You had
tea with Garth, at the Club?'

Her eyes widened. 'You have no need to be
jealous,' she was swift to retort and for answer Paul
reached out for her wrist and she was jerked against
him in a way that was almost rough.

'Little one,' he said warningly, 'just you remember you're mine. I don't know if I want you having
afternoon tea with a handsome fellow like Garth
Helmley.'

Was he serious? Loretta managed a forced and
shaky laugh. 'You have no claim on me yet,' she felt
impelled to say. 'I—' The rest was smothered as his
demanding mouth crushed hers. She quivered within
the strong embrace of his arms, and eagerly recipro-
cated his kiss. Breathless when, after a long while
she was free, she looked up at him with limpid eyes,

searching his bronzed countenance for any sign of anger. Yes, she thought, recalling that the idea had come to her before, Paul could hurt her by his displeasure, and if she married him that was one thing she would have to accept, since it was not feasible that she would never incur his displeasure. But there would be the making up, when he would be contrite about his sternness or his anger, and he would be tender and loving once again.

'I certainly do have a claim on you,' asserted Paul after he had kissed her again. 'The claim of a man whose wife you are soon to be.' His eyes were dark with tender emotion as he added, 'What stronger claim can there be than that, my darling?'

She made no answer, but just snuggled against his coat, thrilling to the gentle caress of his hands and the strength of his body against her. It was bliss, and for a while she had no thought for Lee or Flora as she lifted her face to invite his kiss. She saw the light of amusement in his eyes before he lowered his head to take her lips.

'Don't you keep me waiting too long,' he warned when, after an interlude of passionate love-making, he held her at arms' length, mastery and possessiveness in his manner and his expression. 'You're far too seductive for me to resist you for any length of time, my love.'

So confident! She had not even told him she would marry him—in fact, she had made it clear that she had made no decision one way or another. However, she knew she would marry him in the end . . . and if only Lee and Flora could come together again then there would be no need for any lengthy delay.

It was Paul who broached the subject as they sat, a short while later, drinking sherry on the *stoep* while watching the final splendour of the sun's descent.

'It is odd that you should mention doing something about those two, because I myself had begun to wonder if they could be helped. The stumbling block is, of course, that we don't know what transpired after Flora found the photograph, to cause the break.'

'Or just how serious it is. Lee was willing to get a divorce, remember.'

Paul had poured himself another drink and he spoke as he stood up by the rail, the sherry in his hand. Loretta watched him, as always noticing how immaculate he looked, in a white suit tonight, with a lemon-coloured evening shirt which seemed to accentuate his Arab brownness instead of contrasting with it, as his clothes usually did. His angular, aquiline features, strong and finely-chiselled, even shadowed as they were in the dying light, seemed more handsome than ever, and feathery ripples of sheer happiness sped along her spine. He would certainly be a husband to be proud of! And she wouldn't have been a woman had she not felt a surge of pride and pleasure at the knowledge that she would be envied all her life by other, less fortunate, women.

'What is your opinion of this business?' Paul looked at her, his eyes flickering over her as if he could not resist taking in her beauty even yet again.

'After hearing what Garth had to say, and knowing that the picture was of me, I feel that they ought to be—well—taken in hand, as you might say.'

'You can't be absolutely sure that the picture was yours.'

'No,' she agreed, but went on to say she felt almost sure it was. 'And if so,' she continued with a thoughtful expression, 'then Flora should be told about it.'

It was Paul's turn to become thoughtful. 'You believe that Flora was jealous, and not only that but that she believed, on seeing the photograph, that Lee had been having an affair with another woman?' Paul shook his head bewilderedly.

Loretta frowned and gave a small sigh. 'Lee could have explained, if it was only that.'

'You think there was something else, then?'

She nodded automatically and fell silent while sipping her drink. 'I'll make Lee confide in me,' she said at length and with firm decision. 'But, meanwhile, couldn't you go and talk to Flora?'

'I could, yes.'

'You know where she lives?'

'Sheila Murray will give me her address.' Sheila Murray was an old spinster living alone in one of the smart bungalows which occupied such attractive sites along the road leading to Falburg. Her father had been a farmer and after he died she sold out and bought herself the attractive home in which she now lived. Paul had mentioned her one day when they were passing her house, and he had said that she and Lee's wife had been on the friendliest of terms. 'I guess that Sheila and Flora correspond fairly regularly.'

'Sheila might be able to tell us something, then?'

Paul nodded his head. 'I'd already thought of it,' he said. 'I'll pay her a visit tomorrow morning.'

'Oh, will you, Paul?' with eagerness and a lightening of the shadows in Loretta's eyes. 'She must be as eager as anyone to have Flora back here.'

'Flora was a companion to her; she used to call for her and take her into town.'

'Wouldn't it be great for us all if we could bring about a reconciliation, Paul?' The eagerness was increasing to excitement.

Paul looked at her with tenderness and said quietly, 'Yes, little one, it would be great . . . for all of us.'

Chapter Nine

Because she had made up her mind to question Lee about the break between him and Flora, Loretta told Paul that she wanted to see Lee alone. It was two days after they had been discussing the possibility of effecting a reunion between the estranged couple and already Paul had been trying to get in touch with Sheila. But she had been out on both occasions when he had stopped by, and as his three phone calls had also brought no result he assumed that Sheila had gone away on holiday.

'Lee's a lot better, the doctor said when I rang him this morning, so I agree it's a good idea for you to go alone,' said Paul when Loretta had put her request to him. 'He'll probably be in a fit state to talk, but be prepared for the doctor to turn you out right in the middle of the conversation if he should come into the ward and decide Lee has had enough.'

Loretta nodded her head. 'I'll try to get as much from Lee as I can before that happens.'

She drove herself in the runabout and parked it in the hospital grounds. Lee was sitting up in bed, with the blanket now tucked in instead of being around him.

He smiled as she approached the bed and she saw that although he was very pale and drawn at least his eyes were much brighter than they had been for the past three days.

Loretta sat down on the chair which the nurse had drawn up for her. Lee reached out to take her hand. He seemed far away within seconds, a vacant expression in his eyes.

'Are you feeling better?' began Loretta, curling her fingers around his affectionately.

'A little.' His smile was forced as he added, 'I won't be right for weeks.'

'But you'll soon be home again and then we can help you recuperate.'

Perhaps it was something in her tone which caused him to examine her closely and then to say, 'You and Paul . . . ? I mean, you and he haven't—?'

'Paul loves me,' she broke in gently, not having intended telling him quite so soon in their conversation. He had provided the opening and there was nothing else she could do under the circumstances.

'So he's giving Olga up?'

Loretta nodded. 'Yes, he's finished with her.'

'There's no hope for me then.' A statement and a sigh to accompany it but there was no real pain either in his voice or his expression.

Loretta stared at him for a long moment before

saying, 'Lee—you and your wife—what happened to part you?'

He glanced down to where his fingers were still entwined with hers. 'She found a photograph of you—' He stopped and his mouth went tight. 'I'm not talking about it, Loretta.'

She saw the little beads of perspiration rising on his brow and bit her lip in vexation. How could she persist in questioning him when he was feeling like this? Nevertheless, she did force herself to say, 'Don't you think, Lee, that you were both very foolish?'

He made no answer for a space, but the tightness left his mouth. 'She didn't accept that I still loved you.'

A frown gathered on Loretta's brow. 'You mean, you told her it was me you loved and not her?' she exclaimed disbelievingly.

He swallowed hard. 'It wasn't like that, Loretta. But I had cherished the memory of those idyllic days and weeks you and I had together. I used to take out your photograph sometimes and look at it.' He stopped and shook his head. 'It's something I can't explain to you any more than I could explain it to her. Maybe it was an obsession—I can't say. All I know is that when she walked into the bedroom and saw me holding your photograph I had to say I loved you.'

Loretta's frown deepened, as well it might, for she could make no sense of what Lee was saying to her. 'You loved Flora when you married her?' It was really not a question, since she had already decided that Lee was not the man to marry a woman he did not love.

It was a while before an answer came. 'Yes,' he owned in a low and somewhat husky voice, 'I did love her, very much.'

'Yet you told her, later, that you loved me? What had happened?'

'I've just said—I'd always cherished the memories which you and I gathered together.'

Loretta sighed and shook her head slowly, puzzledly. 'But Lee, dear, you can't allow memories to wreck your marriage.'

'She wouldn't listen!'

'Did you try to explain?'

'I couldn't put over to her what I really felt.' He paused and wiped his brow with a handkerchief he'd had under his pillow. 'I had to say I loved you and always would love you.' He looked directly into her eyes. 'It's true, Loretta—I swear it's true.'

She fell silent, pondering on what Paul had said more than once. What had existed between her and Lee had been more in the nature of a father and daughter relationship than anything else. Of course, Paul had on one occasion—when she had said she did not think Lee had regarded her as a daughter—agreed with her. But the reason was that Paul was regarding her himself through the eyes of a lover so it was only to be expected that he would, at that particular moment, agree that Lee had been similarly affected. For herself—well, she now admitted frankly that she had regarded Lee more as a fatherly figure than as that of a lover. Her love was strong and so was his . . . but it was a very different kind of love from what either of them believed at the time.

And Lee, not yet having reached the same conclusion, was bewildered by the conflicting emotions which assailed him. He truly believed he loved Loretta in the same way as Paul loved her. But it was Flora he really loved. . . .

Loretta said gently, 'So Flora went away believing you loved someone else, someone you'd known long ago?'

He nodded, and she saw that words were difficult for him to voice. But at length he did speak, and sheer unhappiness made his voice so low that she had to lean forward in order to catch the words.

'Can a man love two women at the same time?' He was speaking to himself; it was very plain that he was thinking of Flora and not of Loretta at this moment, this quiet and profound moment.

Loretta knew the opening was just right for her to say, 'Lee, dearest Lee, don't you realise that your love for me is more paternal than anything else?'

For a long, dazed interlude he just stared at her, his eyes wide and yet examining. And suddenly perception seemed to sweep over him; he gave a deep shuddering sigh and lay back against the pillows as if he were exhausted. And at that moment the ward door swung inwards and the doctor was there, white-coated and himself looking rather tired. His eyes went from Loretta to the man on the bed and he frowned. Abruptly he lifted a hand, rather in that way Paul had, imperious and commanding.

'I must ask you to go, Miss Sedgewick. I ought to

have told Nurse that you could stay for only ten minutes.'

Loretta rose from the chair, stooped to touch her lips to Lee's forehead, then quietly went past the doctor into the corridor beyond.

She felt hemmed in in the white-walled corridor, felt as if she wanted to run, to reach the open air and breathe freely again.

And yet, she was sure she had had a successful visit, felt that once Lee accepted what had come to him, he'd then begin thinking of wanting his wife back.

Paul was taking the sun, stretched out on a lounger in the garden when she arrived back. She drove the runabout on to a spare piece of ground at the side of the homestead and walked around to where he was, clad only in shorts and sandals. He sat up, his eyes questioning. There was another lounger a few yards away and she took possession of it, sitting on the edge while she related all that had passed between her and Lee.

'So you believe he's accepted that his interest in you was paternal.' Paul had listened with deep interest and Loretta had seen his expression change several times as she proceeded.

'Yes, I do believe it. He seemed a little stunned at first by the idea, but then his eyes widened as if he had suddenly realised that what I suggested was in fact the true position.' Loretta paused; Paul merely smiled and she continued slowly, 'I can understand his dilemma—or perhaps I should say, uncertainty.

He truly believed he loved me, yet he also knew he'd married Flora for love, so it was no wonder he was bewildered.'

Paul said after a long, thoughtful moment, 'It's my opinion that he was clinging to a memory simply because he couldn't bear to let it go.' His interest was with Loretta suddenly, and she noticed a strange, unfathomable expression in his eyes. 'It's plain to me now, Loretta, that there was something very deep and strong between you and Lee at one time.' His face was taut, and seemed darker, more bronzed, than ever. 'Will it always be there, I wonder?' he added almost to himself and, frightened all at once, she was swift to remind Paul that, as he himself had always maintained, it had been a father and daughter relationship.

'You've just said "at one time,"' she added finally, her anxious eyes wide and appealing. 'Please don't be jealous, Paul,' she begged. 'We both know that Lee is in love with his wife and we both know that there'll be a reunion and that they'll be happy together . . . just as we will be happy together.' Timidly she touched his sleeve. 'I haven't said I'll marry you, Paul, but now I can say I will.'

His face softened miraculously, and in seconds she was in his arms, quivering against him, warm and happy in her own sweet haven, the place to which she could always come when things went wrong—as they must inevitably go wrong sometimes, she thought, for she was expecting to be married to Paul for a very long time.

He looked down into her lovely face, and moments passed before he bent his head and possessed her lips. She pressed close, her arms stealing up to curl around his neck.

'I love you,' she whispered when presently her lips were free. 'Paul, darling, what I felt for Lee was nothing like this! I never craved for—for . . .' She tailed off and hung her head, hiding her expression from him. He laughed softly, a laugh half mocking and half triumphant as, with a finger beneath her chin, he raised her head and she was compelled to meet his eyes. They were filled with tender amusement and his lips were curved.

'So you're craving to be made love to,' he said, taking her face between his hands and holding it within his warm grasp. 'Must we wait, then, my little one? It's out of date to be a chaste bride these days, you know.'

He was laughing at her with his eyes but she was in no doubt that beneath the humour he was serious. She was tempted and he knew it, but he adopted no unfair methods, knowing as he did just how vulnerable she would be should he decide to awaken her desires, as he could so easily do.

Loretta shook her head and moved away. They both sat down again. 'I want to be a chaste bride,' she returned shyly, 'fashionable or not.'

'I'm glad you said that, my love.'

'So you're old-fashioned, too?'

'I oughtn't to be,' he returned with a wry expression which brought forth a question.

'Because you've had so many women?'

His eyes widened, then narrowed. 'My child,' he said sternly, 'a lady with even the smallest notion of delicacy doesn't ask her fiancé things like that!'

Fiancé. . . . Loretta forgot the rest of what he said, forgot it in the thrill of thinking of herself as engaged to be married.

'You've—spoken to Olga?' she ventured after a moment's silence and Paul nodded his head at once.

'I've told her I'm marrying you,' he returned without emotion.

Loretta would have liked to ask how the girl had taken it, but, of course, she refrained from doing so. Nevertheless, she could not suppress her imagination in the same way; she could see the girl's fury, her jealousy, and Loretta felt a trifle sorry for her because it had seemed, until Loretta came along, that Olga would become Paul's wife. The girl herself had believed so, and apparently there were a number of others of the same opinion.

'What are you thinking about, my love?' Paul's quiet voice recalled her from her reverie and she glanced up.

'Of Olga,' she replied frankly and saw his eyes widen again.

'Olga?' interrogatively. 'Why?'

Loretta shrugged self-consciously. 'I just wondered about her. . . .' She trailed off and changed the subject quickly. 'Garth was talking about the polo match next Saturday. I'm very much looking forward to watching it.'

His eyes were perceptive; she blushed, aware that he knew she was curious about Olga. It seemed petty, and yet it was something purely feminine, she admitted to herself.

'You've never seen a match before?'

'No, never. Shall I be nervous do you suppose?'

'Nervous?'

'Of you—I mean, for your safety?'

'You mustn't be, dear. A spill at some time or other's pretty well to be expected if one plays regularly. But more often than not one gets away with a few minor injuries.'

So casual! Loretta found herself wishing he did not play the game, and yet she knew that even when she was married nothing she would say would influence him. Paul would stop playing when it suited *him*, and not before. So this was one of those anxieties she would have to face.

'I think I shall be anxious,' she just had to say.

'You've only just told me you're looking forward to watching the match,' he reminded her with a hint of humour.

'I hadn't thought of the danger.'

'Then don't think of it now,' he advised, rising from the chair and coming towards her. With a sort of careless gesture he took her hand and brought her to her feet. 'You're not to worry this beautiful head about me, my love. I have too much to live for now to take any unnecessary chances.' Bending his head, he kissed her brow, and her cheek, and then her lips. She pressed close, her arms about his waist.

'Paul, oh, if only Lee and Flora can make up their differences! They must! We shall make Flora understand, shan't we?'

He nodded, holding her close as she brought her head to his shoulder. 'Yes, darling, we certainly shall make every effort to do so.'

'I wonder when Sheila will be home?'

'I don't think she'll be away long. This is the first

time I've known her to be away; she's extremely fond of her home.'

'Perhaps Lee will give me Flora's address,' suggested Loretta as the thought occurred to her. 'I'll ask him tomorrow when we go to see him.'

But Lee was not so well as he had been the day before and as she stood by his bed a deep frown creased Loretta's wide brow. She looked at Paul, saw he was frowning too and said softly, 'Has he had a relapse?'

Paul was shaking his head even before she finished speaking. 'He's letting himself go—'

'No! Oh, no, he can't do that!' She looked down at the man on the bed and tears filled her eyes. Her thoughts were running around in circles as one idea after another flashed through her mind. First, she was blaming herself for telling Lee that she and Paul intended to marry. That was the reason for Lee's deliberately trying to lose hold on life. Then she was remembering her conviction that it was Flora he loved and so his deterioration had nothing to do with her, Loretta, after all. Another idea was born, the idea that Lee might be thinking he had killed all his wife's love and, therefore, he no longer wanted to live. She raised appealing, tear-filled eyes to Paul's, and noticed his jaw tighten at her obvious distress. He went out of the ward and she guessed he was going to see the doctor. Loretta spoke to Lee but received no answer, so she turned and spoke to the nurse.

'He's not nearly as well as he was yesterday. What's happened?'

'He very unhappy I think.'

'He said something to you?'

'He ask me to telephone his wife and ask her to come, but she tell me no, she have no wish to come.'

'When was this?'

'Yesterday after you leave here. Just as soon as you leave he ask me to phone.'

'I see. . . .' Loretta turned again to Lee. 'How do you feel?' she inquired in gentle tones. 'Tell me what's wrong, Lee.'

His eyes were glazed; it was plain that he had no desire to speak to anyone as he turned from her and tucked his cheek into the pillow.

Paul returned alone.

'The doctor's off duty and as there's no urgency he can't be called.' He stood by the bed staring down at Lee and a heavy sigh escaped him.

'I've spoken to him but he doesn't want to answer,' whispered Loretta, unashamedly crying now. 'I can't bear to see him so unhappy, Paul. What can we do for him?' She went on to tell him of what she'd learned from the nurse. 'I must see her myself,' she ended. 'I'm determined to do so!'

'Let's call at Sheila's on our way home,' decided Paul. 'She might just be back and able to supply us with Flora's address.' He was whispering even though he and Loretta had moved away from the bed. She nodded and could only hope that the old lady would be home. Moving back to the bed she said goodbye to Lee; he stirred then and looked up into her eyes.

'Don't cry, dear—don't cry.'

'You've got to get better, Lee.'

'Better. . . .' A shuddering sigh escaped him. 'I felt better yesterday, dear, but today I feel very ill.'

'Not ill, dearest Lee, but depressed.'

His eyes became alert. 'You know why?'

'You've been trying to get in touch with Flora. Does that mean you've admitted to yourself that it is her you really love?'

'Yes, Loretta, it is Flora I love . . . in that particular way.'

In that particular way. . . . So he had owned to the fact that his love for Loretta was in fact paternal. She twisted her head to see if Paul had heard. He inclined his head to tell her he'd heard it all.

'Flora will be with you soon,' promised Loretta even while she was wondering if Flora's love for Lee had died. It seemed so strange that she had refused to come and see him in hospital, especially when he had asked for her. Was she heartless? Loretta was asking Paul as they drove away from the hospital grounds.

'No such thing,' firmly and in a louder voice than he normally used. 'Either she's being stubborn or there's some other reason why she can't come.'

'If she's stubborn then she's heartless, as this isn't the occasion for obstinacy!'

'Well, we shall soon know.' He was slowing down and as he slid to a halt Loretta saw the old lady in the garden. Paul had obviously seen her a little sooner.

When they went into the garden she looked up to smile at Paul, who introduced her to Loretta.

'Happy to meet you, dear,' said Sheila. 'I've heard

about you and how pretty you are.' The pale eyes looked her over. 'You're a friend of Lee's, I'm told.'

'Yes, that's right.'

'Sheila,' broke in Paul briskly, 'can we go inside? I'd like a chat with you.'

Sheila looked questioningly at him, her lined face lifted so that she could look directly into his eyes. Loretta took stock of her in the few seconds of silence which followed Paul's request. The woman, though old, was slim and fit—'tough' was the word Loretta found instantly coming to mind. She'd been gardening and the small trowel was still in her long, bony and weathered hand. Her blouse and skirt, in two shades of grey—the blouse being the paler of the two—hung loosely on a body which was rather too sparse of flesh. The hair was grey and dried out with the sun, the curving eyebrows were dark and winging out towards her temples. An impressive face, decided Loretta, with that straight Roman nose, those high glossy cheek bones and the wide mouth, bloodless almost, and dry-skinned.

'Something important, Paul?' Sheila asked curiously, her eyes moving from him to Loretta and then flitting back again.

'Yes.' He nodded. 'It is important.'

They went indoors and through the long, white-walled room to the shady *stoep* at the back. Sheila, who had preceded them, flicked a hand, indicating that they should take a seat. Paul drew forth a rattan chair for Loretta, then sat down himself, stretching out his long legs in front of him. Sheila brought out iced lemonade without asking what they wanted, and placed the cut-glass jug on the table after already having brought out a small silver tray holding three matching glasses. Only then did she speak, after sitting down opposite to Paul.

'What is it, Paul?'

Looking at her, Loretta somehow knew that the woman had guessed at the reason for this visit, and she fell to wondering how much gossip had been going on, and how much Sheila had heard.

'I want to talk to you about Flora,' said Paul quietly.

'Yes?' Again that flick of the eyes in Loretta's direction. 'What is it you want to know—and why?' The voice, somewhat manly and brisk, was now abrupt and demanding. Sheila was not intending to be drawn into anything until she knew the reason first. 'Flora's a young friend of mine whose affairs are not for gossiping about, Paul.'

'Can you imagine me indulging in gossip?' Paul eyed her censoriously, but Sheila merely gave an indifferent shrug of her thin, narrow shoulders.

'I've been hearing plenty of gossip since I returned from Durban only last evening.'

'About what?'

'Lee and Loretta here, and you and Olga. You've broken with her, I'm told.'

'There was really nothing to break. People assumed far too much.'

'And the girl herself, apparently. She's having people believe she's been jilted.'

'Nonsense! Olga has far too much pride for that,' retorted Paul angrily.

'Well, you know how things gather all kinds of

additions when they're passed from mouth to mouth. However, I'm glad you're not marrying the girl. Never could stand her arrogance. It's rumoured,' she went on with another darting glance at Loretta, 'that you and this young lady here are rather more than friendly.'

This statement startled Loretta, for she'd had no idea that anyone would already have come to those kinds of conclusions.

'Loretta and I are engaged,' submitted Paul in his quiet and finely-modulated voice. 'But as you've heard so much gossip perhaps you'd tell me what they've been saying about Loretta and Lee?'

'People wondered why she was here, especially as Lee's separated from his wife.' There was a question this time in the swift glance which she sent to Loretta. 'You knew Lee some years ago, I gather?'

'Seven—almost eight.'

'What made you come here?'

Paul stirred restlessly and before Loretta could answer he began to speak, and in as few words as possible explained what had happened.

'I see. . . . So it's been a complete misunderstanding from the first?' Impatience brought a darkness to her eyes. 'Silly pair! Lee saying he was still in love with you, and Flora running off like that!'

'You can't blame Flora,' submitted Loretta. 'I know I wouldn't like to find my husband looking at a photograph and then telling me he was in love with the girl.'

'He's an idiot! They both are! For two mature people to act in such a stupid way—Bah, they want their heads banged together!'

173

'Flora won't come to see Lee even though he's so ill,' Loretta put in sadly. 'What are we going to do?'

'To tell the truth,' disclosed Sheila, 'I've just made a flying visit to Durban to see Flora and to try to persuade her to come back, especially as Lee is ill. She refused, as you say, Loretta, but it was only because she didn't know everything; she still believed her husband was brooding over the loss of his first love.'

'You'll now tell her what we've told you?'

'Supposing you go to Durban?' suggested the old woman. 'I feel you could do far more good than either Paul or I.'

Loretta nodded in agreement. She looked at Paul, who was taking a drink, and she waited until he had put his glass down.

'Will you take me, Paul?' she asked.

'Of course,' he replied.

A small silence fell as they all took their drinks. Loretta's eyes were appreciative in their examination of the garden with its abundance of colour, its neatly-trimmed hedges of prickly pear or agave. Tall slender trees lined the short drive from the road and these also formed a barrier at the back—presumably the boundary of Sheila's land. Scanning the further distance, Loretta could see the native *kraals* outlined against a line of low hills, the *kraals* from which was heard the mystical throb of the drumbeats at night, when darkness fell.

'I shall want Flora's address from you,' Paul was saying a few moments later as he and Loretta rose to leave.

'I'll get it for you.' Sheila went into the house,

returning quickly with a piece of paper which she handed to Paul. 'Good luck,' she said, and smiled at Loretta for the first time.

'Will you go to see Lee?' requested Paul and Sheila promised to visit him the following day.

'I'll not tell him anything for the present, not until we know for sure that Flora will return to him.'

'She'll return,' from Loretta with emphasis. 'I shall make her!'

Chapter Ten

The following day being Saturday, Paul went off after an early tea to play in the polo match, while Loretta went along a little while later, having arranged to pick Sheila up. It had surprised her to find that the old woman liked to watch such an exciting game, but she was soon to learn that she was among the loudest applauders.

For Loretta, the game was interesting, but she found herself lacking the enthusiasm she initially hoped she would have. She was scared, her eyes almost always on Paul's impressive figure and the magnificent pony he was riding. It seemed to be a very hazardous game, testing every man's strength and ability. During the game she heard bits of the jargon—the ground was 'accurate,' or a comment on the 'buffalo' grass always necessitating certain tactics which, Loretta assumed, were different from what would be used on a ground in England. The shots had a lot of lift and length which, according to Sheila, who was sitting beside her, made for good open polo, whatever that might mean, thought Loretta with a grimace. She heard someone at the back commenting on Paul's play.

'He's obviously deciding on a series of approach hits instead of trying for a big hit.' Then there was a roar of applause as he back-handed a shot from right in the centre of a mêlée and scored a goal.

Loretta was glad when it was over, but Paul only laughed when she confessed to being so nervous that she could not enjoy the game as she should have done.

'Silly girl,' he chided, but with tenderness in his tone. 'Even if I did have a tumble I'd not get hurt.'

'Sheila thoroughly enjoyed it,' she said, bypassing his confident statement.

'She always does. She's a surprising lady, as you will discover when you get to know her better.'

'Are we going to Durban tomorrow? Did you manage to get a flight?'

'Yes—I thought I'd mentioned it.'

'Ought we to let Flora know we're coming?'

'I rather think it would be best just to surprise her,' replied Paul after a moment of considering. 'I have an idea she's going to feel self-conscious— guilty even—and if we warn her of our coming she might just decide to avoid the meeting.'

'Well,' returned Loretta exasperatedly, 'she sounds very foolish to me!'

Paul looked at her with a hint of amusement in his eyes. 'You appear to have forgotten your admission as regards your own attitude, were you to see your husband holding a photograph and hear him saying he loved the girl he was looking at.'

She coloured a little. 'Nevertheless,' she mused after a space, 'I don't think I'd be so stubborn as to go on indefinitely. In any case, I'm very sure I'd not be able to resist a plea like the one Lee made.'

'You'll like Flora when you've met her,' Paul assured her with a smile. 'I feel that you and she will become friends once you're safely married to me and she feels safe.' He looked at her and stooped to kiss the tip of her nose. 'Be kind to her, darling, won't you?'

'Of course, Paul.'

It was much later, when they were on the *stoep* after dinner, that Paul mentioned the matter of announcing the engagement. 'What about giving it out at the Club next week sometime?'

'When there's a dinner dance, you mean?' Excitement brought a quiver to her voice and a hint of delicate pink to her cheeks.

'That would be a suitable occasion. Then there's the matter of the ring. If we stay overnight in Durban we can get one there.'

Loretta found difficulty in speaking, for she still could not fully believe that Paul loved her and wanted to marry her. He had always seemed so far above her, so polished and confident, with that innate arrogance and that air of mastery which both thrilled and awed her and which she would not change if she could.

'I love you,' was all she could say and, as if each knew the desires of the other, they rose from their chairs to come close in a tender, loving embrace.

'And I love you, my darling. . . .' Paul's lips were on hers, as light in their caress as the wings of a moth. She quivered with ecstasy and for a long moment there was silence, Loretta giving herself up to the delight of his love-making. All around them was silence, the brooding, mystic hush so reminiscent of the primordial. Native *kraals* shed twinkling lights as they staggered up the slopes of a distant hill, a hill bathed in silver which now and then darkened as the clouds sped across the face of the moon. Closer to, the giant trees bordering the homestead gardens formed deep purple silhouettes against the mysterious African sky. Loretta stirred in the circle of her lover's arms and a gentle sigh escaped her. He laughed softly, and held her hard and close, possessively, masterfully, a hand sliding over her body to reach the delicate curve of her throat before tilting her chin so that he could look down into the starry depths of her eyes.

'We must go in,' he sighed reluctantly at last.

She nodded her head. 'I suppose so.'

Again he laughed, this time with teasing amusement. 'You don't really want to, though.'

'Nor do you,' she countered.

'Darling,' he murmured after kissing her gently, 'remember what I've said: don't keep me waiting too long. I'm not made of stone, as you should know by now . . . nor, my little one, are you!'

* * *

Loretta had tried to form a picture of Flora—in fact, she had questioned Paul several times as they were on their way to Durban.

'She's pretty—I've already told you so,' he had said.

'Fair or dark?'

'Mid-brown hair and pale skin.'

'Tall?'

'A little taller than you.'

'And she's older. . . .' Nevertheless, Loretta really had no idea what to expect, and the first thing that struck her on meeting the woman was the quietness which seemed to surround her, the perfect peace which emanated from her. There was no other way Loretta could explain her sensations when, after having taken the woman by surprise, she held out a hand and introduced herself as swiftly as she could.

Flora took the hand, staring half in puzzlement and half in inquiry as she said, 'How did you get in here?'

'A woman opened the door. I had seen you here, seen you through the window as I passed on my way up the drive. I guessed it was you, Lee's wife, so I'm afraid I went past the lady and came right in—' She swung around on being aware of the woman who had opened the front door to her.

'My mother,' Flora murmured, but her eyes were glued to Loretta's face.

'How do you do?' murmured Loretta mechanically. She was in a hurry to speak to Flora alone because she sensed that any delay could result in her being politely, but firmly, told to leave. She was meeting Paul in an hour's time at the Elangeni Hotel, and she had no wish to admit to failure.

'Shall I leave you, dear?' Flora's mother's anxiety showed in the glance she cast at Loretta. 'I don't know who this is, but—'

'I have to speak to Flora,' Loretta broke in urgently. 'It's of the utmost importance because it concerns her husband—'

'Lee?' The woman's manner was definitely hostile. 'I think—'

'He loves his wife,' from Loretta on a pleading note. 'I've come to try to effect a reconciliation.'

Silence, with Flora clearly trying to make up her mind and fearfully Loretta waited. But suddenly she felt a wave of determination sweep over her and she added into the silence, 'He loves you dearly, Flora, and I feel sure that you love him. I want to explain, to prove to you that Lee has no love for me in the way he loves you. . . .' Her voice trailed as Flora looked at her mother, the glance plainly asking her to leave the room.

And after that Loretta found her task easy. Flora listened, tears filling her eyes more than once, but valiantly suppressed, so that they never fell on to the pale cheeks. All the time she spoke Loretta was looking at the girl, taking in the clear, youthful skin, the fine bone structure of her face, the firm contours, the high forehead and clear, frank grey eyes. Flora's hair, though a rather nondescript colour, made up for this by its gleaming softness and attractive waves.

'You'll go back to him?' This finally, but Loretta knew the answer she would receive.

'Yes—oh, yes,' softly and contritely. 'I've been a fool, Loretta—I can call you Loretta?'

'Of course,' with a winning smile. 'I hope we shall all four be very good and close friends from now on.'

'Lee was so convincing. . . .'

'About loving me?' Loretta gave a small impatient sigh. 'He was a fool! But I must admit that I myself never realised the kind of relationship which had existed between us, not until Paul convinced me of it.'

A pause followed as Flora lapsed into thought. 'It seems strange for Paul to be marrying at last,' she murmured almost to herself. 'He seemed to be thoroughly enjoying the "bachelor gay" kind of life—Oh, I don't mean—'

'That he was a flirt? I expect he had his moments, like most men do before they finally settle down.'

'It doesn't worry you?' Flora's gaze was interested and examining.

'Of course not.'

'I feel so awful, about Lee, I mean.'

'In your case it was rather different. I had to admit that I'd have felt pretty rotten if I had caught my husband looking at a picture of an old flame. And I'd have felt much worse if, like Lee, he'd said he was still in love with the girl.'

'You're very understanding,' returned Flora in her quiet, rather musical voice.

'I'm just a woman,' rejoined Loretta simply and she held out her hand after a swift glance at her wristwatch. 'I must be off now, Flora. You'll not waste any more time, will you?'

The other girl shook her head at once. 'Not a moment more than is necessary!'

'We're returning tomorrow—'

'And I could come with you?' Again Flora shook her head. 'No, even better, I can get a plane this evening. . . .'

Paul was in the lobby of the luxury hotel when Loretta entered, her face revealing, which brought forth the words, as Paul came forward to join her, 'So it was easy, then?'

'Very, once I'd managed to explain that Lee looks on me rather as a daughter.'

Paul laughed and Loretta's heartstrings caught. How attractive he was!

'I'll bet Sheila will give them both a dressing down.'

'They'll not need it. They both know they've been fools.'

'All's well that ends well. And now my love—' as he tucked her arm into his, '—we shall go and buy the ring. What have you in mind for preference?'

'I have always imagined a diamond solitaire.' She was shy, and turned her head away. She felt his hand take hers and squeeze it tenderly.

'We're in the right country for diamonds,' was all he said and together they sauntered out from the hotel into the pale afternoon sunshine. Loretta, having such a wide choice put in front of her, took time and care and eventually the velvet-lined box was in her fiancé's pocket. Then they took a leisurely stroll through the beautiful gardens of Durban's waterfront, but it was much later, as they walked together in the gardens after dinner, that Paul put the lovely ring on Loretta's finger.

'Forever, my little one,' he murmured close to her cheek. 'Always remember that you're mine now till the end of your life.'

She sighed happily. 'I want nothing more, my darling,' she assured him when, after he had kissed her until she was breathless, he finally gave her the chance to speak.

'Nor I, my lovely, my adorable . . . wife.' Paul bent to take her lips again, lips still rosy from his recent not-too-gentle love-making. 'Didn't I tell you that all would eventually resolve itself?'

'Yes, but—oh, at one time, Paul, it did seem that I'd have had to marry Lee.'

Paul gave her a little shake. 'Do you suppose I'd have let you?' he asked her grimly.

'It was my own choice.' She paused, saw he had become thoughtful—almost broodingly so, and she added slowly, 'You were having to admit it, weren't you, Paul?'

After a long silence he nodded his head. 'Yes, I was. I felt I was in total command one moment, but the next—Well, I confess I was afraid, knowing that, if you should decide to marry Lee, then you would do it.' He held her at arms' length to look into her eyes. 'You know, dear, I feel now that you'd not have plunged into marriage with Lee without some considerable thought. You loved me, so how were you going to be faithful to Lee?'

'I'd never have been *un*faithful,' she protested frowningly.

'My dear child, you'd have been unfaithful every time you thought of me . . . and that would have been often.'

Loretta feigned indignation. There was a sparkle in her eyes as she retorted, 'What an opinion you have of yourself! What makes you so sure you'd have always been on my mind?'

'For the simple reason, my darling, that you would always have been on my mind.'

She coloured adorably, then buried her face in his shoulder. 'You're so right, Paul, and so wise. Yes, you'd have always been on my mind.'

Paul lifted her face from his shoulder and for the next few minutes rained fierce and passionate kisses on her lips, her throat, her firm young breasts through the thin material of her evening blouse.

'When will you marry me?' he asked after saying the engagement would be announced immediately they returned to their home.

'When . . . ? Er—in a m-month . . . ?' She did not want to seem overly eager, so she added slowly, 'Or perhaps a little longer?' She stopped rather abruptly on seeing his expression, clearly revealed by the lights flaring out from the roof of the hotel building.

'A *month!*' he ejaculated. 'What on earth do you want all that time for?'

She coloured, and then laughed. 'A week, then,' she countered mischievously, thinking he would say that was not quite long enough.

But he said with a sigh, 'If you really need a week,

185

then I suppose I must wait. However, as we can buy the dress here, tomorrow morning, I don't see why you can't be ready in a couple of days.'

He was teasing, she realised, and once again countered by saying casually, 'All right, darling, we'll make it the day after tomorrow. We don't need to have any guests, or a party, or any fuss at all—' She got no further, because of the little shake he gave her. But the next moment he was kissing her with all the tenderness he felt for her, was caressing with gentle mastery that thrilled even while it tempted, was murmuring the kind of endearments that brought delicate colour flooding to her cheeks.

'A fortnight, my little one,' he was saying later in a throaty bass tone of voice. 'If the preparations are going to last a day longer than that—then I shan't be responsible for what happens.' He held her from him and in his eyes there was a sort of challenging mockery; but a deep, deep tenderness and love were there, too. 'Do I make myself clear, my darling?'

'Absolutely clear,' she replied and her own voice was husky, but more with emotion than passion. 'I want you, Paul, darling, just as much as you want me—and so—so I shall be ready in a—a fortnight.' She was embarrassed at the confession she had made, and because he understood her so well, Paul said nothing more but merely drew her head close again and nestled it against his shoulder.

Silhouette Romance

IT'S YOUR OWN SPECIAL TIME

Contemporary romances for today's women.
Each month, six very special love stories will be yours
from SILHOUETTE. Look for them wherever books are sold
or order now from the coupon below.

$1.50 each

Hampson	☐ 1	☐ 4	☐ 16	☐ 27	Browning	☐ 12	☐ 38	☐ 53	☐ 73
	☐ 28	☐ 52	☐ 94			☐ 93			
Stanford	☐ 6	☐ 25	☐ 35	☐ 46	Michaels	☐ 15	☐ 32	☐ 61	☐ 87
	☐ 58	☐ 88			John	☐ 17	☐ 34	☐ 57	☐ 85
Hastings	☐ 13	☐ 26			Beckman	☐ 8	☐ 37	☐ 54	☐ 96
Vitek	☐ 33	☐ 47	☐ 84		Wisdom	☐ 49	☐ 95		
Wildman	☐ 29	☐ 48			Halston	☐ 62	☐ 83		

☐ 5 Goforth	☐ 22 Stephens	☐ 50 Scott	☐ 81 Roberts
☐ 7 Lewis	☐ 23 Edwards	☐ 55 Ladame	☐ 82 Dailey
☐ 9 Wilson	☐ 24 Healy	☐ 56 Trent	☐ 86 Adams
☐ 10 Caine	☐ 30 Dixon	☐ 59 Vernon	☐ 89 James
☐ 11 Vernon	☐ 31 Halldorson	☐ 60 Hill	☐ 90 Major
☐ 14 Oliver	☐ 36 McKay	☐ 63 Brent	☐ 92 McKay
☐ 19 Thornton	☐ 39 Sinclair	☐ 71 Ripy	☐ 97 Clay
☐ 20 Fulford	☐ 43 Robb	☐ 76 Hardy	☐ 98 St. George
☐ 21 Richards	☐ 45 Carroll	☐ 78 Oliver	☐ 99 Camp

$1.75 each

Stanford	☐ 100	☐ 112	☐ 131		Browning	☐ 113	☐ 142	☐ 164	☐ 172
Hardy	☐ 101	☐ 130			Michaels	☐ 114	☐ 146		
Cork	☐ 103	☐ 148			Beckman	☐ 124	☐ 154		
Vitek	☐ 104	☐ 139	☐ 157	☐ 176	Roberts	☐ 127	☐ 143	☐ 163	
Dailey	☐ 106	☐ 118	☐ 153	☐ 177	Trent	☐ 110	☐ 161		
Bright	☐ 107	☐ 125			Wisdom	☐ 132	☐ 166		
Hampson	☐ 108	☐ 119	☐ 128	☐ 136	Hunter	☐ 137	☐ 167		
	☐ 147	☐ 151	☐ 155	☐ 160	Scott	☐ 117	☐ 169		
					Sinclair	☐ 123	☐ 174		

6 brand new
Silhouette Special Editions
yours for 15 days–Free!

For the reader who wants more…more story…more detail and description…more realism…and more romance…in paperback originals, 1/3 longer than our regular Silhouette Romances. Love lingers longer in new Silhouette Special Editions. Love weaves an intricate, provocative path in a third more pages than you have just enjoyed. It is love as you have always wanted it to be—and more —intriguingly depicted by your favorite Silhouette authors in the inimitable Silhouette style.

15-Day Free Trial Offer

We will send you 6 new Silhouette Special Editions to keep for 15 days absolutely free! If you decide not to keep them, send them back to us, you pay nothing. But if you enjoy them as much as we think you will, keep them and pay the invoice enclosed with your trial shipment. You will then automatically become a member of the Special Edition Book Club and receive 6 more romances every month. There is no minimum number of books to buy and you can cancel at any time.

Silhouette Romance

Coming next month from
Silhouette Romances

Another Eden by Anne Hampson

Richard was Susanne's world . . . but after the accident had left her blind, it was his brother Nick at her hospital bedside, opening up a brighter future than she ever imagined.

Loving Rescue by Dixie Browning

It was Lacy's first visit to Guatemala . . . her luggage and handbag stolen, was she also in danger of losing her heart to the enigmatic Jordan Stone?

Make-Believe Bride by Nancy John

Would Belinda play substitute wife for Welsh farmer Adam Lloyd when her scheming identical twin walked out on him and Adam mistook her for his new bride?

Runaway Wife by Brenda Trent

When fashion designer Kati Autumn arrived in Mexico City, the last person she expected to meet was Raul, her estranged husband—who wanted her back again.

African Enchantment by Andrea Barry

Armand de Vincent was as exciting and dangerous as Africa itself. How could Patricia be absolutely dedicated to her dancing when she found herself so attracted to this playboy!

Mistletoe And Holly by Janet Dailey

Christmas festivities were the furthest thing from Leslie's mind . . . until she met Tagg and found herself filled with a desire to give the ultimate gift—her heart.

READERS' COMMENTS ON SILHOUETTE ROMANCES:

"I would like to congratulate you on the most wonderful books I've had the pleasure of reading. They are a tremendous joy to those of us who have yet to meet the man of our dreams. From reading your books I quite truly believe that he will someday appear before me like a prince!"

—L.L.*, Hollandale, MS

"Your books are great, wholesome fiction, always with an upbeat, happy ending. Thank you."

—M.D., Massena, NY

"My boyfriend always teases me about Silhouette Books. He asks me, how's my love life and naturally I say terrific, but I tell him that there is always room for a little more romance from Silhouette."

—F.N., Ontario, Canada

"I would like to sincerely express my gratitude to you and your staff for bringing the pleasure of your publications to my attention. Your books are well written, mature and very contemporary."

—D.D., Staten Island, NY

*names available on request